A Howard W. Sams PUBLICATION   20440

abc's of
TRANSISTORS

by George B. Mann

abc's of

TRANSISTORS

GEORGE B. MANN

HOWARD W. SAMS & CO., INC.
THE BOBBS-MERRILL CO., INC.
INDIANAPOLIS · KANSAS CITY · NEW YORK

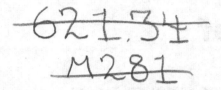

SECOND EDITION

FIFTH PRINTING—1969

PREFACE

Very few developments have electrified the electronics industry as much as the transistor. Back in the '20's, radio was hailed as some sort of magic carpet which carried one's voice all over the world. In the '60's, the transistor has shrunk the size of this magic carpet; by replacing vacuum tubes with transistors, manufacturers can produce receivers that are just a shadow of their former selves. Transistors have made a reality of the wristwatch radio. What other miracles can they evoke? Only time will tell!

Today's electronics technician or student must know transistors as well as he knows vacuum tubes. Much literature has already been written about transistors. Why, then, did I decide to add this book to the stack? The reason is plain—because of the definite need expressed by technicians and students for a basic, easily-understood volume on the subject. The remarkable reception of the first edition seems to imply that it has met this need. In this new edition, later material and new devices have been included.

abc's of Transistors is precisely that—an ABC of transistors. It is simple enough that the student and technician should have no trouble understanding it, yet not so simple as to insult the reader's intelligence. In short this book is a primer of transistors.

This book does not involve you, the reader, in a labyrinth of technical information, nor does it dwell on specific servicing procedures for each type of transistor circuit. I believe that if you understand basic transistor circuits, you will know how to service them. If you carry away an understanding of the fundamentals of transistors and a desire to learn more about them, this book will have served its purpose.

GEORGE B. MANN

CONTENTS

CHAPTER 1

CHAPTER 2

CHAPTER 3

CHAPTER 4

CHAPTER 5

CHAPTER 6

CHAPTER 7

CHAPTER 8

CHAPTER 9

1

TRANSISTOR FUNDAMENTALS

Transistor is a term applied to a large group of solid-state devices having three or more terminals connected to the semiconductor material. The transistors of primary interest to the service technician are the NPN and the PNP junction types used in automobile radios, audio preamplifiers, audio amplifiers, portable radios, table-model radios and television receivers. Transistor fundamentals, basic circuits, circuits in present-day home entertainment equipment, practical servicing procedures, and special handling considerations—as presented in this book—will be helpful to the technician interested in servicing transistor equipment.

The NPN and PNP transistors currently used in home entertainment equipment are essentially two junctions of semiconductor material. A study of basic transistor fundamentals should therefore begin with the semiconductor material.

SEMICONDUCTORS

The semiconductor material in most transistors employed in radio and audio equipment is either germanium or silicon. Semiconductors, as the term implies, fall in a category between good conductors and good insulators. The semiconductor material is not used in its pure state. Controlled amounts of certain impurities are added which, by

7

imparting certain conduction properties to the material, produce what is known as a doped semiconductor.

The doping material (impurity) may be one of two general types:

1. Donor impurity—donates electrons to the semiconductor. Donor impurities produce N-type semiconductors.

2. Acceptor impurity—accepts electrons from the semiconductor material. Acceptor impurities produce P-type semiconductors.

The primary difference between P and N material is the type of charge movement. In N-type material, current is produced by a movement of electrons or negative charges; in P-type material, current is produced by a movement of holes or positive charges.

ELECTRONS AND HOLES

Electron is a familiar term associated with the electronics field. Current in wires, tubes, and other components is generally accepted to be by electrons, which are negatively charged particles. The term *hole* is fairly new to electronics and has a meaning opposite from the electron. Hole denotes a positive charge, or the lack of an electron—just as the term *vacuum* denotes the lack of air. The hole or positive charge can be measured and is mobile within the semiconductor material.

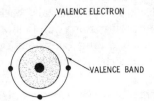

Fig. 1-1. Exaggerated sketch of an atom, showing the various parts.

To describe the foregoing more fully, we must touch briefly on the atomic structure. Atoms are made up of a nucleus surrounded by rings of electrons. Each ring of a particular atom consists of a specific number of electrons. The electrons in the outer ring lie in a band termed the valence band (Fig. 1-1). A discrete level of energy in this band provides the force that binds all the electrons in the valence band of one atom to the electrons in the valence bands of other atoms and makes up the crystal structure (Fig. 1-2).

If atoms with five valence electrons (Fig. 1-3A) are added to the structure shown in Fig. 1-2, the material would then contain free

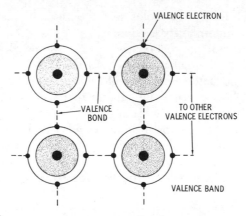

Fig. 1-2. Composition of crystal structure from atoms.

electrons that would not be held by a valence bond. This addition can be performed in semiconductors by adding a *donor* impurity that produces an N-type semiconductor. The electrons (negative charges) not bound in the crystal structure can now be used as charge carriers. In N-type material, the electrons are called *majority* carriers because the majority of the current will be composed of electrons. This statement presupposes that current can be composed of holes, and this supposition is correct. The holes are minority carriers in N-type semiconductors.

(A) Donor   *(B) Acceptor*

Fig. 1-3. Donor and acceptor atoms at a junction.

In the same manner that a donor impurity donates electrons to the semiconductor material, an acceptor impurity (Fig. 1-3B) causes the semiconductor material to accept electrons, adding acceptor atoms (Fig. 1-3B) produces a P-type semiconductor. In the P-type semiconductor, there are atoms that lack an electron in the valence band. This lack of an electron is termed a hole, or positive charge. The hole, being the lack of an electron in the valence band of an atom, does not move out of this band; therefore, conduction takes place in the valence band. This action can occur in solids only (such as P-type semiconductors); it does not apply to vacuum-tube theory. Because the majority of electric current in P-type semiconductors is composed of holes, the holes are the majority carriers and the electrons are the minority carriers.

To understand this theory, the reader should think in terms of positive and negative charges. (1) An electron is a negative charge that will be attracted by and will move toward a positive charge and (2) the hole is a positive charge that will be attracted by and will move toward a negative charge.

An electron leaving the valence band will leave a hole in the valence band, and an electron-hole pair will be formed. The electron and the hole will have equal charges but opposite polarities. If an electron fills a hole in the valence band, the charges will be canceled.

The main points to remember are that electrons are negative charges and that holes are positive charges. Both can move and, as such, can be current carriers. In N-type semiconductors, the electrons are the majority carriers; in P-type semiconductors, the holes are the majority carriers. Current in a semiconductor is composed of negative or positive charge movement, or both negative and positive charge movement.

JUNCTION OF P AND N SEMICONDUCTORS

Transistor operation is normally based upon the action of the carriers at the junction of P and N materials. A pictorial method of describing the action of the carriers at a junction will probably be the easiest to follow. For this purpose, the blocks labeled N and P in Fig. 1-4A will represent the doped semiconductor materials. The N material is shown as having electrons as majority carriers, and the P material is shown as having holes as majority carriers.

In the N material or the P material, a net charge balance is maintained by the even distribution of majority carriers throughout the material. It must be recognized that the majority carriers are bound into the crystal structure of the semiconductor. The material itself has no charge, and carriers will not flow between two types of material if they are just placed in physical contact. The term junction implies that the materials are bound together at the molecular level by a process such as fusion or melting.

When P and N semiconductors are formed together to produce a junction, the majority carriers near the junction move toward each other and cancel out (Fig. 1-4B). Because of this canceling action at the junction, a charge has now been established between the semiconductor materials. Since some of the majority carriers (electrons in the N-type and holes in the P-type) have been effectively

(A) Two types of semiconductor materials and their associated carriers.

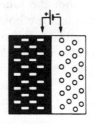

(B) Action that takes place when junction is produced.

(C) Battery showing polarity of charge at junction as a result of the union of N and P materials.

Fig. 1-4. Action of the carriers at a junction.

canceled, the material at the junction assumes a positive charge in the N semiconductor material and a negative charge in the P semiconductor material. Remember, as we previously noted, the majority carriers were bound in the crystal structure and, before the junction was formed, there was an even distribution of these carriers in the individual semiconductor materials. Therefore, the material by itself had a zero net charge.

The electrons in the N material now are repelled by the negative charge in the P material, and the holes (positive charges) are repelled by the positive charge in the N material. These majority carriers therefore maintain positions back from the junction. The charge and its polarity at the junction are represented by the battery in Fig. 1-4C. This charge, or potential, is extremely small—in tenths of a volt—but does produce an effective potential hill or barrier to the passage of the current carriers. To pass from one side of the junction to the other, the electron or hole must gain energy equal to this potential hill.

The sources of external energy that can move the carriers across a junction may be radiation in the form of heat, light, or X rays; or the source may be a more usual one, like a battery or power supply.

FORWARD AND REVERSE BIAS

The PN junction acts as a one-way valve, or rectifier, to the flow of carriers. There is through the junction a forward, or low-resistance direction, and a reverse, or high-resistance direction. Current in the low-resistance direction is called forward bias; current in the high-resistance direction is called reverse bias.

The potential hill at the PN or NP junction, represented by the battery at the junction in Fig. 1-4C, must be overcome before the carriers can move. When a battery is connected so that it aids or increases the potential hill at the junction, the carriers are pulled farther away from the junction (Fig. 1-5A). The minus charge of the battery attracts the holes to the right, and the positive terminal of the battery attracts the electrons to the left. Such a reverse-biased junction can have a d-c resistance reading in the megohm region.

As the applied voltage is increased, the potential hill increases, and the resistance of the junction also increases. Unlike a resistor, the reverse-biased junction increases its resistance as the voltage increases.

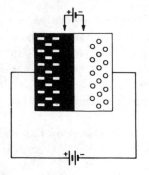 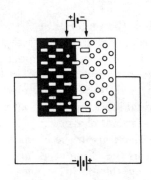

(A) Result of connecting a battery to aid, or increase, the potential hill (reversed biasing).

(B) Result of connecting a battery to reduce the potential hill (forward biasing).

Fig. 1-5. Relation between the applied voltage and the potential hill.

The resistance of a reverse-biased junction depends upon the applied voltage. The current in a reverse-biased junction is relatively constant. As the voltage across a resistance is changed, the current changes. With a junction diode, however, the reverse-bias voltage produces a resistance change, but the current remains nearly the same. This condition can be shown by the Ohm's law formula $I = E/R$. Thus, if E (voltage) increases across a resistor and if the resistance is constant, I (current) will increase. If E increases and if the resistance increases proportionately (as it does in the junction diode), then I will remain constant.

NOTE: The same diode will present different resistance readings on ohmmeters with different internal battery voltages or with different internal resistances.

The forward biasing of a junction will reduce the potential hill. When a battery with opposite polarity from that of the potential hill is applied to the junction, the carriers are moved up to the junction (Fig. 1-5B). Holes and electrons now flow across the junction. This action results in a current in the external circuit. Another way of describing this action is by saying that the battery will inject positive charges into the P material and will inject negative charges into the N material.

The forward bias is different from the reverse bias because the voltage necessary to overcome the potential hill is rather small; but once this potential is reached, the current has little opposition. As current increases, the resistance of the junction decreases. The applied voltage remains nearly the same. (A small rise in voltage is necessary to overcome the resistance of the semiconductor material.)

Summary

Resistance of a reverse-biased junction depends upon the applied voltage and is relatively independent from the current.

Resistance of a forward-biased junction depends on the current and is relatively independent from the applied voltage.

Forward bias is a voltage applied to a junction to overcome the potential hill. This bias is applied in what is termed the low-resistance direction.

Reverse bias is a voltage applied to a junction in the high-resistance direction. This produces an increase in the potential hill.

The action of the carriers at a junction should be well understood because the transistor is, in effect, two PN junctions. If the physical structure of the junction is changed, a variety of interesting results can be achieved. The junction transistor is one result.

THE JUNCTION TRANSISTOR

The transistor is composed of an emitter E, a base B, and a collector C. The arrangement in Fig. 1-6 is for an NPN transistor with an N-type emitter and collector and a P-type base. Notice that the base region of the transistor is drawn thin in comparison to either the emitter or the collector region. There is a reason for this thin base region: it affects both the majority and the minority carrier action at the junctions.

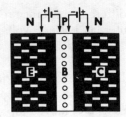

Fig. 1-6. An NPN-type transistor.

The proper base-to-emitter bias for an NPN transistor is shown in Fig. 1-7A. When the base-to-emitter battery is connected in the forward direction, the majority carriers are forced up to the junction, and a current is produced between the base and the emitter. The holes move into the N material, and the electrons move into the P material. Recombination takes place at the junction, but the combining of electrons and holes can also take place after the carriers have passed this barrier. The existence of such minority

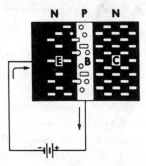

(A) The proper base-to-emitter bias for an NPN-type transistor.

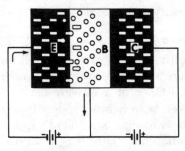

(B) Action caused by connecting a second battery in the reverse bias direction of an NPN-type transistor.

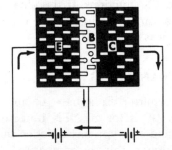

(C) Effect of a thin base region on transistor action.

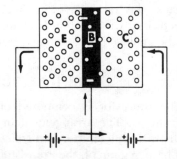

(D) The PNP-type transistor showing reversed action.

Fig. 1-7. The effect of forward and reverse biasing of a transistor.

14

carriers (electrons in this example) in the base region is of prime importance to the operation of a transistor.

When free electrons exist in the emitter region of an NPN transistor, they are majority carriers; but when these same electrons cross the barrier into the base region, they are considered minority carriers. These electrons eventually combine with holes in the base region unless some field or force intervenes.

In Fig. 1-7B a second battery is connected to the transistor. This battery is connected in the reverse-bias direction and has thus caused the carriers to move away from the base-to-collector junction. A wide base region, such as shown in this figure, permits all of the electrons from the emitter to recombine with holes in the base region. In this situation we actually have two diodes, one forward and one reverse biased; and no transistor action takes place.

In Fig. 1-7C the base region has been made thin. The electrons forced into the base region by the forward bias at the emitter-to-base junction are now attracted by the positive charge of the N-type material at the junction of the collector and base. A large number of electrons now traverse the base region and reach the collector before recombination takes place. A small number of electrons and holes do recombine in the base region to produce a current in the base-to-emitter circuit. This current is referred to as bias current or base current.

Summary

The forward bias of the emitter-to-base junction produces electron flow into the base region. The proximity of the base-to-collector junction causes the electrons to be attracted to the collector. The result is a current between the emitter and the collector.

The PNP transistor action is identical to the action of the NPN except that the roles of the electrons and the holes are reversed, as shown in Fig. 1-7D.

The forward bias on the base-to-emitter junction causes holes to be injected into the base region. The negative charge of the collector causes these holes to progress through the base region and into the P-type material of the collector. Recombinations of some holes with the electrons in the base region result in a small current in the base circuit.

CURRENT CONTROL

The forward bias or the injection of carriers into the base region controls the amount of current in the collector circuit. Increasing or decreasing the electron flow from the emitter region to the base region of an NPN transistor will increases or decrease the electrons available to the collector circuit. For a PNP transistor, the availability of holes to the collector is controlled by the injection of holes into the base from the emitter.

The forward bias at the emitter-to-base junction provides energy to the carriers on each side. Because the energy is added to the carriers, they can overcome the potential hill more easily. There are two ways to look at this effect. (1) The energy is added to the carriers to permit them to overcome the potential hill. (2) The height of the potential hill is reduced by the applied voltage. Incidentally, the potential hill does not decrease to zero. As the potential hill gets smaller, the number of recombinations increases to maintain a barrier.

The collector current depends upon the number of available minority carriers in the base region. If more carriers cross the emitter-to-base junction, more minority carriers will be available in the base region or will be available to the collector. Increasing the collector voltage does not increase the number of available carriers. Therefore, the collector current will remain relatively constant as the collector voltage changes.

The height of the potential hill between the emitter and the base is determined by the emitter-to-base bias. This height of the potential hill also determines the collector current. Decreasing this hill increases the available carriers, and increasing the hill decreases the available carriers. Thus, the collector current can be controlled by controlling the base-to-emitter bias. Amplification is not necessarily produced by this action.

AMPLIFICATION AND GAIN

Amplification and gain, whether they be of power, current, or voltage, are measures of the difference between the input and the output. The transistor can perform as an amplifier in various circuit configurations, and in each, the basic operation of the transistor itself will remain the same.

The input circuit of a transistor is associated with the injection of carriers into the base region. The output circuit is associated with the flow of carriers from the emitter to the collector. The larger portion of the current is between the emitter and the collector, and only a small current will exist between emitter and base. A circuit with two meters, such as the one in Fig. 1-8, can be used to demonstrate this effect.

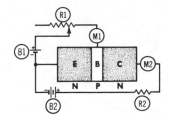

Fig. 1-8. The basic operation of an NPN transistor as an amplifier.

In this circuit, meter M1 will indicate the bias current or the current between the base and emitter. Meter M2 will indicate the collector current. When resistance R1 is changed, the current in M1 will change, but the current change in M2 will be much larger. A small change in the base current will produce a larger change in the collector current.

The voltage drop across resistor R1 will be small, not greater than the voltage of battery B1. The voltage across resistor R2 will be much larger, particularly if the voltage of battery B2 is larger. In this circuit then, a voltage gain has been realized.

In practice, the circuitry can be arranged to produce either voltage or current gain or both; but in either case, the basic operation of the transistor remains the same.

GERMANIUM AND SILICON TRANSISTORS

Two basic types of transistors are presently being produced. They receive their name from the semiconductor material from which they are produced—germanium and silicon.

The primary differences between these two types is the maximum allowable operating temperature and the voltage required to overcome the potential hill.

The bias voltage applied to the emitter-to-base junction of a germanium transistor to produce forward current will be approximately one-tenth to two-tenths of a volt, whereas, the silicon transistor bias will be approximately four-tenths to six-tenths of a volt.

Operating temperature for the silicon transistor is nearly twice that of the germanium. The maximum junction temperature for a germanium transistor is about 110°C. The silicon transistor can be operated as high as 200°C.

Note—These temperatures are maximum and in many instances the recommended maximum values may be considerably lower than these temperatures.

2

PHYSICAL
CONSTRUCTION

The operation of many electronic devices can be explained by physically breaking down the item. For example, each component (grid, plate, cathode, and heater) of a vacuum tube can be removed and inspected. This method lends strength to the understanding of vacuum tubes.

A transistor junction, the heart or functioning part of the transistor, is so small that good observation of it requires a microscope; even then, there is some doubt whether anything will be observed, other than a small piece of metal with three or more contacts fastened to it. Even the power transistor types contain a small wafer of semiconductor with very small contact areas. Little information can be gained from a visual examination of the collector, base, or emitter.

The transistor is a solid-state device in which current control takes place inside a solid crystal of specially fabricated metal. Purity of the metal throughout the processing is extremely important in order that the desired properties can be maintained. The exposed transistor crystal with leads attached will function properly in a circuit; but exposure to moisture, gases, light, or heat will soon affect the operation of the crystal. The unit must be hermetically sealed in some type of envelope or case if consistent operation is to be expected over a long period of time.

ENVELOPE OR CASE

The envelope or case may be constructed of such non-porous types of materials as metal, glass, plastic, ceramic or epoxy. A number of these materials were used in early production types. More

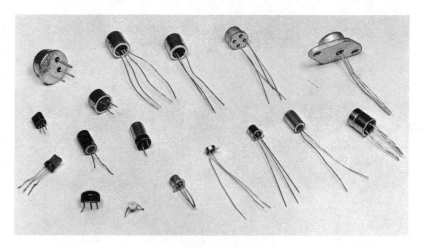

Fig. 2-1. Examples of various transistors.

recently, the structure of the envelopes that enclose the semiconductor has been fairly standardized throughout the industry. Some general types of transistors in use today are shown in Fig. 2-1. The three small cases on the right in Fig. 2-2 are examples of transistors designed for use in miniaturized equipment. The large transistor on the left is a standard TO5 case used for size comparison.

The transistor case must be constructed of an opaque substance that excludes light, since light will affect the operating characteristics of the transistor. (The one exception is the phototransistor; because light is the current-control medium, a portion of the envelope must be transparent.) Metal is used in many envelopes because it is easy to shape, excludes light and most other forms of radiation, and is an extremely good conductor of heat.

The case of the transistor is hermetically sealed to exclude contaminants. Many transistors contain an inert gas or a powder that conducts heat from the semiconductor to the case. Therefore, the amount of power the transistor can handle is increased.

The epoxy case is used for many economy types because of its low cost and ease of fabrication. Epoxy is a good insulator, is a fairly good conductor of heat, and can be made opaque by the addition of special pigments.

SHOCK

Transistors are not shockproof. Although they can withstand a great deal of abuse, they should not be subjected to an undue amount. The transistor usually is mounted in equipment such as a

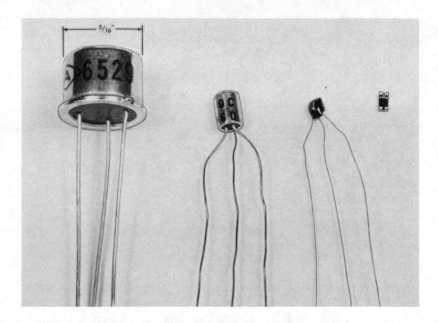

Fig. 2-2. Examples of miniature transistors.

portable receiver; and if the receiver is dropped, the case absorbs most of the shock. The transistor should be handled rather carefully, since it can be damaged by being dropped on the bench or floor. If you do drop a transistor, the chances are that it is not damaged—but don't be surprised if it is.

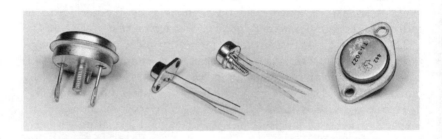

Fig. 2-3. Several types of power transistors.

POWER TYPES

The power transistor, because of its construction, permits maximum dissipation of heat. The transistor is heat sensitive, since its operating characteristics change as its operating temperature changes. Therefore, the design of a power-transistor envelope is closely associated with the amount of power that must be dissipated. A variety of power transistors that portray the differences in case styles is shown in Fig. 2-3.

The envelope of the power transistor is constructed of a good heat conductor, such as aluminum, copper, and/or combinations of heat-

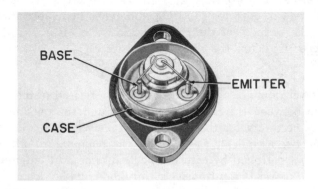

Fig. 2-4. Construction of a power transistor.

conducting metals. The construction of one type of power transistor is shown in Fig. 2-4. The case is formed of copper or copper alloy, and the collector of the junction is mounted directly to this case.

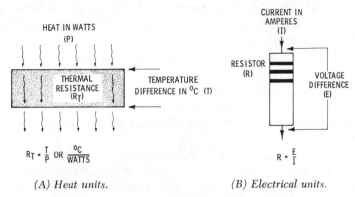

(A) Heat units.   (B) Electrical units.

Fig. 2-5. Similarity between electrical units and heat units.

This direct contact between collector and case provides a maximum of heat transfer from junction to case.

One of the parameters (measurement or constant) encountered in the transistor specifications is the *thermal resistance*. This is a measure of how well the heat is conducted away from the junction. The unit of thermal resistance is usually stated as the number of degrees centigrade difference between the surfaces of a material for every watt of heat energy that is conducted through it. The equation is $R_T = $ °C/Watts.

The similarity between electrical units and thermal or heat units is shown in Fig. 2-5. The thermal resistance (R_T) is calculated the same as electrical resistance (R). The heat in watts (P) is similar to the current in amperes (I). The difference in temperature (T) between the surfaces of the thermal resistance (R_T) is similar to the voltage (E) across the electrical resistor (R).

$$R = E/I \text{ and } R_T = T/P$$

The power rating of a transistor is directly related to the thermal resistance between the transistor junction and the outside of the case. It is necessary for the heat to be removed from the vicinity of the junction as quickly as possible. The temperature of the case can then be controlled by external heat sinks or heat radiators.

The total power that a transistor can safely handle depends upon the efficiency of the heat sink or heat radiator. When a transistor is operated without a heat sink, the power input must be reduced to protect the transistor. High power output requires that large amounts of heat be dissipated into some form of heat sink. A few of the arrangements for increasing the heat dissipation of power transistors are shown in Fig. 2-6.

The heat sink of Fig. 2-6A is both a heat sink and a radiator. Note that the radiator is insulated from the chassis. In Fig. 2-6B the heat sink is also insulated from the main chassis. The transistors in Figs. 2-6A and 2-6B are both fastened directly to the heat sink. This metal-to-metal contact affords maximum heat transfer to the heat sink.

In Fig. 2-6C the transistor is mounted on the receiver chassis, but is insulated from the chassis by the glass fiber pad. Contact is made to the collector by a solder lug clamped directly to the transistor case.

When properly mounted to the heat sink, the transistor can operate at its rated output level. If the heat transfer is reduced by improper mounting, if the size of the heat sink is reduced, or if air circulation is blocked, the transistor can be ruined. When a heat

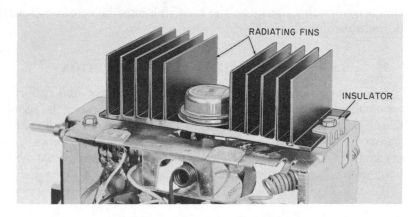

(A) Heat sink using radiating fins.

(B) Insulated portion of chassis used for a heat sink.

(C) Receiver chassis used as a heat sink.

Fig. 2-6. Three types of heat sinks.

sink is used with a transistor, the heat sink must be considered part of the transistor.

LEAD AND TERMINAL IDENTIFICATION

A few transistor types will have the base, emitter, and collector terminals identified with B, E, and C on the case next to the terminals. The transistor shown in Fig. 2-7 has the terminal identification stamped into the case. However, the number of transistors thus marked are few, and most unfamiliar types will require a basing diagram for lead identification.

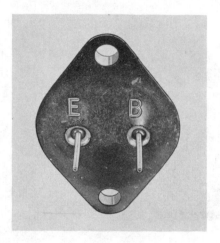

Fig. 2-7. Bottom view of a power transistor, showing terminals.

The power transistor shown in Fig. 2-7 is the type generally found in automobile radios, converter power supplies, and other power applications. The case of this transistor has been standardized by most manufacturers. The metal case is the collector terminal, and the metal pins are the emitter and base terminals.

General standards have been adopted for the most often-used types. These types fall into three groups and can easily be recognized when they are encountered.

The first type consists of those with a color dot on the side. This dot is usually red and identifies the collector terminal. Fig. 2-8 shows a type of basing with three leads or terminals in a straight line and evenly spaced from each other. The collector terminal is the one nearest the dot, and the base terminal is in the center.

Another popular type is shown in Fig. 2-9. The three terminals are in a line, and there is a wide spacing between the collector and

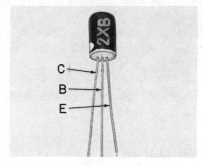

Fig. 2-8. Transistor with uniformly spaced leads.

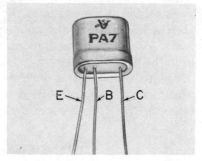

Fig. 2-9. Transistor with uneven spacing between leads.

the base. This type of transistor is employed extensively in transistor portable receivers.

The type of lead arrangement that will be encountered most often is shown in Fig. 2-10. The triangular arrangement is generally identified as shown, but, some transistors have a different terminal arrangement. Be sure of the identification by checking a lead identification guide.

Fig. 2-10. A triangular arrangement for the transistor leads.

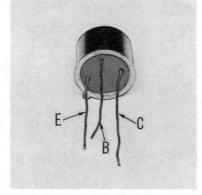

(A) Bottom view.

(B) Identification drawing.

Fig. 2-11. Lead identification.

Unless otherwise stated, the lead identification drawing will show the transistor as viewed from the lead side as shown in Fig. 2-11. When a lead such as the collector is connected to the case it is usually identified on the drawing or by a statement such as the one below the drawing.

Terminal identification diagrams can be obtained for all types of transistors and should be used to positively identify the terminals before the transistor is connected into a circuit.

TRANSISTOR OUTLINES

The outline or physical dimensions for a transistor are provided in most specifications. This information is supplied primarily for

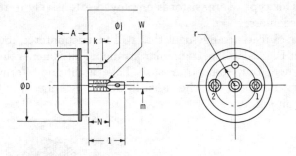

SYMBOL	INCHES MIN.	INCHES MAX.	MILLIMETERS MIN.	MILLIMETERS MAX.	NOTES
A		.520		13.21	
ØD		1.250		31.75	
Øj		.140		3.56	
k		.312		7.92	1
1	.610	.710	15.49	18.03	
m		.190		4.83	
N	.375	.500	9.53	12.70	
r	.345 NOMINAL			8.76	
W					2

NOTES:

1. INSULATED LOCATOR PIN.

2. 10-32 UNF-2A. MAXIMUM PITCH DIAMETER OF PLATED THREADS SHALL BE BASIC PITCH DIAMETER .1697" (4.31 MM) REFERENCE (SCREW THREAD STANDARDS FOR FEDERAL SERVICES 1957) HANDBOOK H28 1957 P1.

THIS OUTLINE DOES NOT MEET THE MINIMUM CRITERIA ESTABLISHED BY JS-10 FOR REGISTRATION.

Fig. 2-12. Specification for the TO36 case style.

design applications but it is also informative for the hobbyist and lets the service technician know if a particular transistor replacement will fit in the space provided.

Most of the registered types have a case style that is designated by a TO number such as TO36. This means Transistor Outline number 36 and gives only the physical dimensions. The data that is provided for the TO36 case style is shown in Fig. 2-12.

3

BASIC TRANSISTOR CIRCUITS

Up to this point the diode or transistor has been represented by a square block that is divided into P and N areas, or emitter, base, and collector areas. The schematic of an electronic circuit must employ different symbols to represent each of the different semiconductor devices. In order to read a schematic it is necessary to understand the meaning of each symbol.

SYMBOLS

The basic semiconductor device is the diode, represented by a bar and an arrow. The diode, or rectifier symbol, is shown in Fig. 3-1. The bar is the cathode and the arrow is the anode. The arrow on the symbol indicates the direction in which positive charges will flow. *Remember that current in a semiconductor can be composed of either a flow of positive charges or a flow of negative charges or both.*

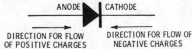

ANODE   CATHODE

DIRECTION FOR FLOW
OF POSITIVE CHARGES   DIRECTION FOR FLOW OF
NEGATIVE CHARGES

Fig. 3-1. The diode or rectifier symbol.

On all symbols for solid-state devices, the direction indicated by the arrow will be the direction for flow of positive charges during the normal operation of the device.

NOTE: The Zener diode is an exception to this rule since it might be said to operate in an abnormal mode when compared to the electrical action in usual semiconductor devices.

The arrow on the semiconductor symbol can be very helpful in determining the polarity of voltage applied to a device. When the device is normally conducting, the arrow will point toward the negative terminal. In the blocking state, the arrow will point toward the positive terminal.

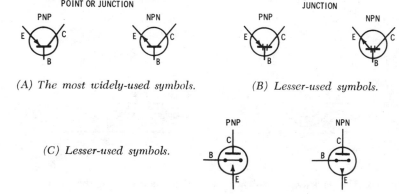

(A) The most widely-used symbols.

(B) Lesser-used symbols.

(C) Lesser-used symbols.

Fig. 3-2. Commonly accepted transistor symbols.

The circuit symbols for the PNP and NPN transistors are shown in Fig. 3-2. The symbols in Fig. 3-2 are generally accepted, and can be used either with or without the enclosing circle. The other symbols in Figs. 3-2B and 3-2C are used to a lesser extent but will be encountered from time to time.

POLARITY OF TERMINALS

The polarity of voltage applied to the PNP transistor is the opposite of that applied to the NPN. In Fig. 3-3 the PNP and NPN symbols are shown with the relative polarity of voltage that exists between each of the terminals.

The transistor can be operated in three circuit configurations—common base, common emitter, and common collector. The configurations are also referred to as grounded base, grounded emitter, and grounded collector. The term "common" or "grounded" refers

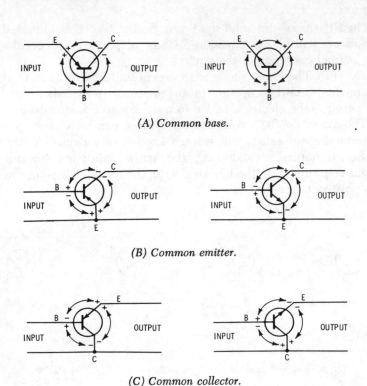

(A) Common base.

(B) Common emitter.

(C) Common collector.

Fig. 3-3. The polarities of voltages applied to transistors in the three circuit configurations.

to the terminal that is common to both the input and the output circuits. In Fig. 3-3A the symbols are positioned in common-base configurations. The input is applied between the emitter and the base, and the output appears between collector and base.

In Fig. 3-3B the emitter is the common terminal. The signal is applied to the base terminal, and the output is taken from the collector.

Fig. 3-3C shows the common-collector configuration, which is also referred to as an emitter follower. The base is the input terminal, and the emitter is the output terminal. This configuration is the least popular of the three configurations. It is used primarily to match a high impedance to a low impedance.

The polarity of voltages applied to the terminals of the NPN transistors is the same for each of the three configurations; only the points of input and output are changed. The polarity of voltages applied to the NPN transistor is the exact reverse of the polarity applied to the PNP types.

30

Two simple rules can be employed to remember how each of the three transistor configurations are connected in a circuit.

1. The base must be one terminal of the input circuit.
2. The collector must be one terminal of the output circuit.

Notice that the arrow on each symbol points from a positive to a negative polarity. This is true for all transistor circuit applications in which the transistor is normally conducting.

TRANSISTOR BIAS

The bias of a diode junction has been described as the presence of current or the application of voltage in a forward or reverse direction (forward or reverse bias). The bias of a transistor is the voltage applied to, or the current between, the emitter and base. This bias determines the operating characteristics of the transistor, and can be considered as being either current bias or voltage bias, or both. The description used depends upon the one that best describes the circuit being considered.

The current bias of a transistor will vary from a few micro-amperes to a few hundred microamperes. The bias voltage will seldom exceed a maximum of one volt, and part of this voltage is made up of the IR drop through the semiconductor material of the emitter and base. Most transistor specifications will list the transistor bias in terms of current in the base circuit.

The forward current at the emitter-to-base junction controls the current between the emitter and collector. Increasing the base current increases the current between the emitter and collector. Decreasing the base current decreases the current between the emitter and collector. The arrows in Fig. 3-4 indicate the direction of electron flow for NPN and PNP transistors. The emitter current

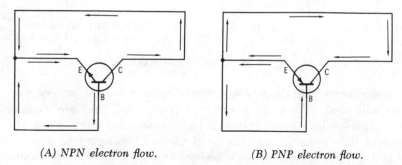

(A) NPN electron flow.   (B) PNP electron flow.

Fig. 3-4. Direction of electron flow for transistors of opposite conduction types.

in both transistor types is equal to the base current plus the collector current.

Common-Emitter Biasing

The circuit you will encounter most often is the common-emitter configuration. The common-emitter circuit has a distinct bias advantage in that one battery will supply both bias in the emitter circuit and power in the collector circuit.

Various biasing arrangements are shown in Fig. 3-5. The circuit of Fig. 3-5A provides a constant-value bias current. Resistance R1

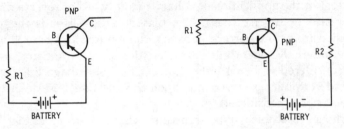

(A) Constant-current bias method.

(B) Constant-current bias with d-c compensation.

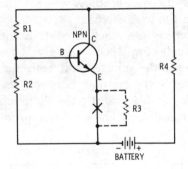

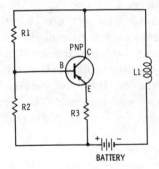

(C) Voltage-divider biasing with d-c compensation.

(D) Voltage-divider biasing with current feedback.

Fig. 3-5. Methods of biasing common-emitter circuits.

is much larger than the base-to-emitter resistance. The battery voltage will produce a given current in resistor R1, and any change in base-to-emitter resistance will have almost no effect upon the current. This is a constant-current method of biasing a transistor.

If the characteristics of the transistor change or if a new transistor with different characteristics is substituted, the same amount of current will not provide the proper operating point. For most applications, the circuit must be so designed that variations within the transistors themselves or variations between the same types will not have a detrimental effect upon circuit operation.

Figs. 3-5B, C, and D show biasing arrangements that provide d-c compensation for transistor variations. In Fig. 3-5B, resistor R1 is connected from collector to base. An increase in collector current will lower the voltage at the collector because of the increased drop across collector load R2. The reduced voltage at the collector reduces the bias; and as a result, the collector current decreases. This action tends to stabilize the circuit and permits wider tolerance components to be used.

In Figs. 3-5C and 3-5D, a voltage-divider arrangement provides a proper bias condition. Resistor R3 is often placed in series with the emitter to provide current feedback. When the load resistance is relatively large, the current change through R3 is small. In Fig. 3-5D, the load is shown as an inductor. Because there is little d-c voltage drop in this circuit, R3 now becomes important in maintaining the operating characteristic of the stage.

Emitter resistor R3 in Fig. 3-5C causes the emitter to follow changes in the collector current. As the collector current increases, the emitter voltage level rises, moving closer to the potential on the base. This decrease in potential difference between base and emitter reduces the bias current and tends to return the transistor to its correct operating characteristic.

The emitter resistor is used in most amplifier circuits because it is particularly useful in stabilizing the bias. The emitter resistor is also used to control thermal runaway in power stages (refer to Temperature Compensation in Chapter 6).

Common-Collector (Emitter-Follower) Biasing

The common-collector circuits in Figs. 3-6A and 3-6B are identical. In the circuit in Fig. 3-6A the emitter, which is the output terminal,

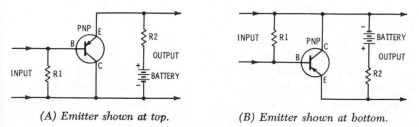

(A) Emitter shown at top.   (B) Emitter shown at bottom.

Fig. 3-6. Method of biasing common-collector circuits.

is at the top right. In the circuit in Fig. 3-6B the collector is at the top right in the conventional manner. Resistor R1, the base-to-emitter junction, and load resistor R2 form a series load across the battery. The collector-to-emitter path and resistor R2 form another series circuit. Because input current and output current both exist in load resistor R2, it is common to both circuits. Increased current in the collector will move the emitter potential nearer to the base potential. The increased IR drop across R2 will reduce the current through resistor R1 and through the base-to-emitter junction. The reduction in bias current will prevent large current changes from taking place in the collector.

This emitter resistor serves as the load resistor, and current feedback is nearly 100 percent. The emitter-follower circuit is extremely stable.

Common-Base Biasing

The common-base circuit requires two voltage-supply points or two batteries, one for power and one for biasing. In Fig. 3-7 resistor R1 and battery A give the correct operating bias. The bias current from battery A flows through resistor R1, the emitter, the base, and back to the battery. The output current path is from battery B through battery A, resistor R1, the emitter, the collector, load resistor R2, and back to the battery. In this circuit, the input and output currents differ only by the amount of bias current in the base circuit.

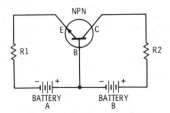

Fig. 3-7. Biasing arrangement for the common-base circuit.

The emitter and collector circuits are practically independent from each other, although the same current exists in both. The force producing the input current is produced by battery A, and the force producing the output current is supplied by battery B. The collector current in resistor R1 provides a current feedback that tends to stabilize the transistor stage. Higher temperatures will increase both the collector current and the voltage drop across R1; thus the bias current will be reduced. This action tends to return the transistor to its proper operating point.

AMPLIFICATION

The meaning of amplification can be extended to cover a great deal of territory. For instance, a relay that requires only a small wattage for its operation can control hundreds of watts by simply closing or opening contacts. Relay action, even though an on-off sequence, can be considered as being amplification. Transistors can be made to perform as on-off switches at low speeds or at speeds in excess of those obtainable mechanically.

The change generally referred to as amplification is a constant but smooth change of signal that is reproduced in its entirety. The term "amplification" includes signals that are increased or decreased in voltage, current, and power, or in any combination of these units. Amplification for any one stage may be as high as $\times 1000$ or as low as $\times 3$, and even less than one (<1 or $\times 0.85$).

Amplification is an expression of the difference between the input and the output signals of a circuit or of a series of circuits. Amplification is equal to the output current or voltage level divided by the input current or voltage level and is also equal, in the case of signals, to the change in output level divided by the change in input level. Chart 3-1 lists the relation between the three circuit configurations and their gains and impedances. The figures and notations are relative to each other; for instance, in the common-emitter circuit, the input resistance is lower than that of the common-collector circuit, but is higher than the input resistance of the common-base circuit.

Chart 3-1.

Characteristics of the Three Amplifier Configurations.

Characteristics	Common Base	Common Emitter	Common Collector
Voltage Gain	Medium (100 to 200)	High (300 to 600)	<1
Current Gain	<1 (.98)	Medium (20 to 100)	Medium (20 to 100)
Power Gain	Medium	High	Low
Input Impedance	Extremely Low	Low	Extremely High
Output Impedance	Extremely High	Medium	Extremely Low
Phase Change Input to Output	0°	180°	0°

Common-Emitter Amplifier

In the common-emitter circuit of Fig. 3-8A, the input (bias battery A) and the output voltage source (battery B) are equal in voltage. A variable resistor (R1) is used to adjust the bias to 1 milliampere. This arrangement establishes the levels of current in the input (1) and output (2) circuits.

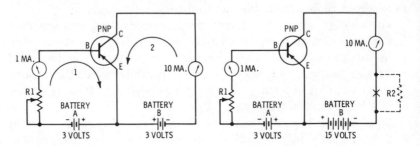

(A) With a 3-volt collector supply.   (B) With a 15-volt collector supply.

Fig. 3-8. The common-emitter amplifier.

With a static gain of ten, the collector current will be 10 ma. This action is termed a static current gain because both the input and the output have static values. One milliampere of current in the input controls ten milliamperes in the output. If the input current is reduced to 0.8 ma and if the output current drops to 8 ma, the change will be 2 ma in the output divided by 0.2 ma in the input, or a dynamic current gain of 10.

In Fig. 3-8B supply battery B has been changed to 15 volts, and the collector current remains at 10 ma. (The current in the collector circuit is relatively independent from the collector voltage.) A resistance R2 can be inserted into the collector circuit to produce an IR drop. This voltage will vary as the input varies, and a voltage gain will be produced. Because of the small voltage necessary to change the base current, the voltage amplification can be quite high. Voltage gains over 100 are not unusual for a transistor amplifier.

Common-Base Amplifier

Chart 3-1 lists the current gain of the common-base circuit at about 0.98. This is a gain of less than one because there is more current in the input circuit than in the output circuit (Fig. 3-9A).

The current in the input circuit is composed of the output current plus the bias current. The output current (in either circuit) is collector current only. Observe that the base lead theoretically has two

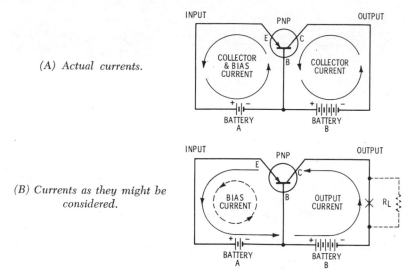

(A) Actual currents.

(B) Currents as they might be considered.

Fig. 3-9. Current paths in the common-base amplifier.

collector currents of opposite polarity; actually, these currents cancel each other and leave only the bias current in the base lead.

The current paths of Fig. 3-9A can thus be described as shown in Fig. 3-9B, in which the output current exists in both circuits. Although the same current exists in both circuits, it must be considered as being two currents, the input current and the output current.

The collector current is controlled by the amount of bias or signal current existing in the emitter-to-base junction. The impedance of the collector circuit will be determined by the collector supply voltage—an increased supply voltage will increase the output impedance. A load, such as resistor R_L inserted into the output circuit in Fig. 3-9B, will have an IR drop (collector current × resistance) across it that will be greater than the voltage which moves this same amount of current in the input circuit. A voltage gain is thus realized from input to output.

Common-Collector (Emitter-Follower) Amplifier

Fig. 3-10A shows the basic circuit for a common-collector amplifier. The input signal is applied to the base and collector, and the output is taken from the emitter and collector.

Fig. 3-10B shows that the output lead is separated from the input lead by the emitter-to-base junction. The voltage between the emitter and the base will change only about 1 volt between collector cutoff and full conduction; therefore, the voltage of the output signal will remain almost the same as the voltage of the input signal, but

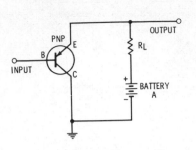
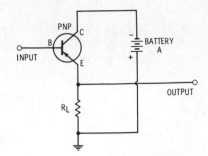

(A) *The basic common-collector*
amplifier.

(B) *A common-collector amplifier with*
the collector ungrounded.

Fig. 3-10. The common-collector amplifier.

the current in the output circuit will be much greater than the current in the input circuit.

The circuit is called an emitter follower because of the action of the emitter. As the input voltage on the base of the transistor in Fig. 3-10B becomes more negative, the current in the transistor increases. This increased current produces a larger voltage drop across emitter resistor R_L. Thus, the changes in the emitter voltage tend to follow the changes in the base voltage.

The emitter follower has a current gain close to that of the common emitter; but, because there is no voltage gain, the power gain is much less. The main advantages of this circuit are the very high input and very low output impedances that make this circuit useful as an impedance-matching device.

OSCILLATORS

The operation of an oscillator can best be described as that of an amplifier, in which a portion of the output energy is returned to the input to produce a cyclic change in the amplifier conduction.

All amplifiers have power losses due to current in the resistance of the wiring, resistors, capacitors, and coils, and in the amplifying device itself. These items all consume energy and dissipate it as heat (I^2R loss). This energy loss is replaced by a battery or other power source. Additional energy must also be supplied to produce an amplified version of the input signal.

The energy supplied to an amplifier is in the form of direct current. When the energy losses in an amplifier are replaced in proper time relation to the input signal, oscillation can take place. Oscillator action is similar to a self-propelled swing. When children first learn to swing, they find it difficult to apply the right energy at the right time and cannot swing very high. After a good deal of practice, they swing very well. (In fact, many of them swing too well.) It's not the amount of energy they supply to the swing, but the manner in which it is applied that makes the difference.

Because a push is required to keep an oscillator operating, it is a form of swing. One type of oscillator requires an outside push, much like one child pushing another in a swing. The bi-stable, or flip-flop multivibrator is an example. Circuits for special applications can be so designed that, for each externally applied push, they will oscillate for part of a cycle, for one cycle, or for a number of cycles.

Of more immediate interest is the free-running oscillator, in which a portion of the amplified output is returned to the input. When the amount of energy returned to the input is equal to and in phase with the signal-energy losses, the amplifier will become unstable. If the feedback is increased beyond this point, the amplifier will oscillate.

The transistor amplifier has been described in its three basic circuit configurations. Since an oscillator is simply an amplifier that has a feedback arrangement for producing a repetitive cycle, there are, therefore, three basic oscillator configurations. They are shown in Fig. 3-11. The operation of transistor oscillators is considered more fully in Chapter 5.

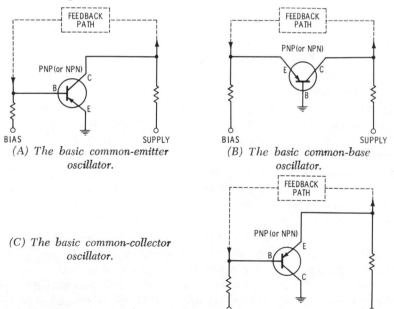

(A) The basic common-emitter oscillator.

(B) The basic common-base oscillator.

(C) The basic common-collector oscillator.

Fig. 3-11. The three basic oscillator configurations.

4

THE TRANSISTOR
AMPLIFIER

Transistor amplifier circuits differ considerably from the familiar vacuum-tube circuits. At the same time there is a reasonable amount of similarity between the two. This might be a good place to point out some of the more outstanding differences and similarities between transistor circuitry and vacuum-tube circuitry.

The transistor has been described in three circuit configurations. The vacuum tube can also be connected in three basic configurations. These configurations are: common cathode, common grid or grounded grid, and common plate or cathode follower. The comparisons are shown in Fig. 4-1. For each vacuum-tube configuration there are two transistor configurations, one for the PNP type and one for the NPN type. The two types of transistor, PNP and NPN, employ opposite polarity voltages and are referred to as complementary types.

The transistor circuit in Fig. 4-1A is the common-emitter circuit that is used almost exclusively for most amplification purposes, just as the common- or grounded-cathode vacuum-tube circuit is also used extensively. The remaining common base and common collector circuit configurations in Fig. 4-1 are used for more special applications, such as impedance matching to and from transmission lines or in place of matching transformers between amplifier stages.

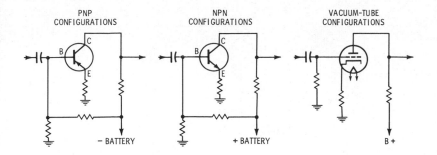

(A) Common emitter—common cathode.

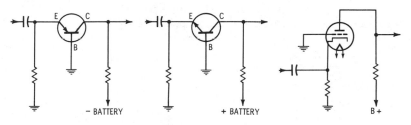

(B) Common base—common grid.

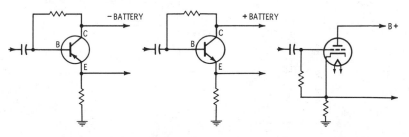

(C) Common collector—common plate.

Fig. 4-1. Transistor circuit configurations and their vacuum-tube counterparts.

AMPLIFIER CIRCUIT RECOGNITION

A familiar tube circuit can be redrawn into another form that will be almost unrecognizable. The circuits used with the transistor can be even more unfamiliar. First, the circuits are new; and second, they can be arranged in two ways, with a PNP transistor and with an NPN transistor.

If the common-emitter circuit is drawn as in Fig. 4-2A and if an NPN transistor is used, the circuit will closely conform to what we are accustomed. The positive battery terminal is connected to the

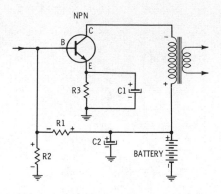

(A) The common-emitter amplifier
circuit with the negative battery
lead grounded.

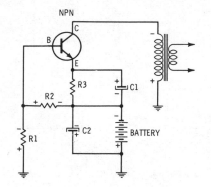

(B) The circuit of (A) wih the positive
battery lead grounded.

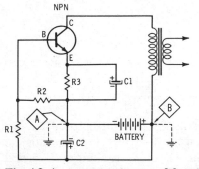

(C) The circuit of (A) and (B) showing
alternate points of grounding.

Fig. 4-2. A common-emitter amplifier circuit, showing different grounding points.

collector. Bias is obtained from the tapped bleeder made up of
resistors R1 and R2. The bias current path to the base of the transistor is from the positive battery terminal through resistor R1.

42

This same circuit can be rearranged to look like Fig. 4-2B. The grounding of the battery terminal is the only difference between this circuit and the one in the previous paragraph. The bias current path is still through resistor R1 except that in this circuit the path is from ground to the base. The same circuit is reproduced in Fig. 4-2C without a ground reference. Point A is the ground used in Fig. 4-2A, and point B is the ground used in Fig. 4-2B.

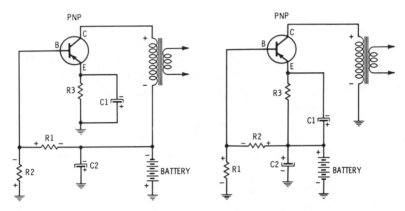

(A) Positive battery terminal grounded.

(B) Negative battery terminal grounded.

Fig. 4-3. A common-emitter amplifier circuit using a PNP transistor.

If a PNP transistor is used in this circuit, two drawings can again be made, one with the positive terminal grounded as in Fig. 4-3A and one with the negative terminal grounded as in Fig. 4-3B.

Compare the PNP circuit with the NPN circuit and notice that the current is reversed in all the components. Therefore, all of the electrolytic capacitors must be reversed when the transistors are changed from PNP to NPN. The reversal of current direction and voltage polarity does not exist for vacuum tube circuitry; therefore, transistor circuits that have no parallel in vacuum-tube circuitry can be produced. Nevertheless, the circuits of transistor equipment are quite similar in many respects to those in vacuum-tube equipment.

INPUT AND BIAS

A signal can be coupled to a transistor stage in a number of ways. Each stage is designed for a particular purpose; and the efficiency of the coupling, the biasing of the stage, the amount of gain desired, and the component cost are all considered.

The most efficient system of coupling a signal to a transistor is with a transformer that will provide a correct match between the signal source and the transistor. Although the transformer may be the most efficient, it has certain drawbacks, such as cost, weight, and limited frequency response. Because of the high gain of the transistor, a less efficient coupling system can be used and there are many systems from which to choose. They will be described in this chapter.

SIGNAL FEEDBACK

When a portion of an amplified voltage or current is returned to an earlier point in the circuit for the purpose of controlling the stability, frequency response, bias, or impedance of the circuit it is referred to as signal feedback.

An arrangement for providing feedback in a single transistor stage is shown in Fig. 4-4A. Resistors R1 and R2 are used as a voltage divider to bias the transistor and, at the same time, they become

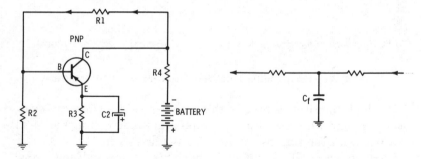

(A) A circuit which accomplishes biasing and feedback simultaneously.

(B) A frequency-selective network that
replaces R1 in (A).

Fig. 4-4. Bias stabilization and signal feedback.

part of a feedback system for the signal. The signal at the collector is impressed across resistors R1 and R2, and part of the output signal is also applied to the transistor base.

The signal at the collector is 180° out of phase with the signal on the base, and the feedback now is degenerative. Resistor R1 can be replaced by a network like the one shown in Fig. 4-4B. If the values of the capacitor and resistors are varied, the feedback can be made frequency selective. If capacitor C_f is made large, the signal can be bypassed to ground and no signal feedback will take place. However, the d-c bias stabilization will still be maintained.

NOTE: Observe that the load R4 is a resistance. This type of feedback circuit is seldom used with an inductive load. The d-c voltage drop across an inductor is not great enough to provide sufficient bias feedback. Bias stabilization is the primary purpose of collector-to-base feedback.

The collector-to-base feedback of the signal is used principally in amplifiers designed to produce a particular frequency response, such as phonograph preamplifiers and high-fidelity sound systems.

Collector-to-base feedback is often used in transformer-coupled output stages to counter the effect of rising transformer impedance at the higher frequencies.

R-C COUPLED AMPLIFIERS

The input circuit in Fig. 4-5 is used more in audio amplifiers than probably any other circuit. This is an R-C coupled input with an electrolytic capacitor to block the d-c voltage from the previous stage. The electrolytics in such transistor stages range from about 1 mfd to 100 mfd. Since the transistor is a low impedance device, the high capacitance is needed to pass audio frequencies.

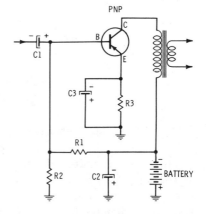

Fig. 4-5. A very common R-C coupled amplifier circuit.

Coupling capacitor C1 in Fig. 4-5 may be connected in either polarity, depending on whether the d-c voltage at the take-off point of the preceding stage is positive or negative with respect to the voltage on the base of the transistor.

Fig. 4-6A is another R-C coupled stage in which R2 is part of the bias network and acts as the volume control. The resistance of R2 becomes a current divider for the incoming signal. The signal current is divided into two paths, as shown in Fig. 4-6B.

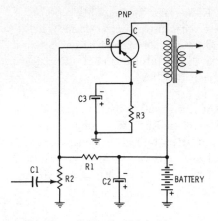

(A) The volume control used as a
current divider.

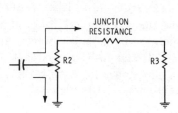

(B) The current division paths.

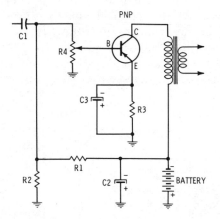

(C) The volume control used as a
voltage divider.

Fig. 4-6. Different types of volume-control circuits.

The volume control of Fig. 4-6C is a voltage-divider type. The signal is developed as a voltage across resistor R4. Moving the slider changes the signal voltage at the transistor base and, at the same time, also changes the bias of the transistor. The signal level and the bias change simultaneously (less signal and less bias) and cause less battery power to be consumed on low volume than on high volume.

TRANSFORMER-COUPLED AMPLIFIERS

The transformer is used for coupling when high efficiency and proper impedance matching are important. However, the trans-

former is more expensive than the resistor and capacitors necessary
to couple two amplifier stages, particularly when special transformers are required to obtain the desired frequency response.

Many functions, such as accurately matching the output impedance of one transistor stage to the input of the next, are fulfilled
extremely well by the transformer. With good matching, the maximum gain of the transistors can be approached.

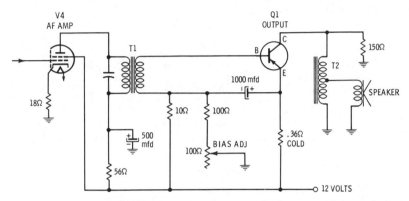

Fig. 4-7. An example of a vacuum-tube stage driving a transistor stage.

A good example of transformer impedance matching is the coupling between the audio-amplifier and power-output stages of a
hybrid auto radio. The diagram of such a circuit is shown in Fig. 4-7.
The audio amplifier is a vacuum tube with a rather high output
impedance, and the output stage is a power transistor with a very
low input impedance. The difference between the two impedances
is so great that, without the transformer T1 (or some form of im-
pedance-changing device), tube V4 cannot provide adequate drive
signal to the base of transistor Q1. The transformer T2 in the collector circuit of the transistor is used to match the collector impedance
to the speaker impedance.

DIRECT (D-C) COUPLED AMPLIFIERS

The main advantage of d-c coupled amplifiers is that they elimi-
nate transformers and coupling capacitors. These latter two devices
tend to limit the frequency response of an amplifier. The d-c amplifier will amplify signals from zero frequency to the high limit im-
posed by the amplifying device (transistor or tube) and by the
associated wiring. In other words, direct coupling is quite a desirable
feature in an amplifier.

Because high-voltage d-c supplies are needed, direct coupling has never been very popular in vacuum-tube circuitry. Each stage must have a higher supply voltage than that of the preceding stage; thus, the final signal must have an extremely high d-c component.

The ideal system would be to have a small d-c change above and below a given reference level, amplify this changing voltage, and end up with an amplified change that still swings above and below the original reference point.

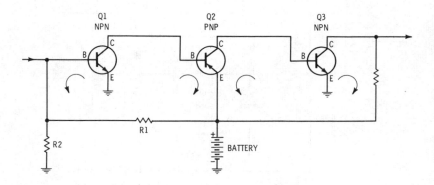

Fig. 4-8. A simplified d-c amplifier.

A transistor can operate as a d-c amplifier. A simplified version of a d-c amplifier using PNP and NPN transistors is shown in Fig. 4-8. The arrows indicate the direction of electron flow.

The single battery supplies the power to all of the d-c coupled transistors in Fig. 4-8. Transistor Q1 is biased from the bleeder circuit of R1 and R2. The bias of transistor Q2 is controlled by the current in the collector of Q1. Similarly, Q3 is biased by the current in Q2.

Any current change at the first transistor Q1 is amplified greatly at the last stage. This high amplification is a property of the transistor d-c amplifier. However, high amplification is also a detriment because transistors are temperature sensitive; therefore, any change in conduction due to a change in temperature will also be greatly amplified. A high-gain d-c amplifier must have some system of compensating for temperature changes.

The circuit in Fig. 4-9 is the audio portion of a transistor portable receiver. Audio amplifier Q4 is direct-coupled to output transistor Q5. Transistor Q4 is biased near cutoff to permit only a small current to exist in the collector of Q4 and in the base of the following stage. This current provides the bias for output transistor Q5.

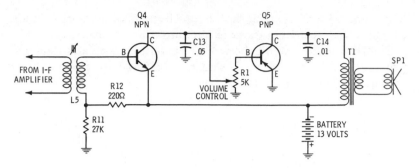

Fig. 4-9. A d-c coupled amplifier employed in a receiver.

The volume control not only controls the signal level, but acts as a divider for the bias current. The signal and bias are increased or decreased simultaneously; and at zero signal setting, output transistor Q5 is cut off. This system provides a saving in battery current because the amount of current depends on the volume setting.

Transistor Q4 operates as the detector and first audio amplifier. The transistor is biased near cutoff; therefore, practically no conduction takes place between the base and emitter. The base-to-emitter junction acts as a diode and blocks the current on the negative swing of the i-f signal, but conducts on the positive swing. These current pulses are amplified in the collector circuit. The r-f is by-passed to ground by the .05-mfd capacitor (C13), leaving an audio signal with an amplitude great enough to drive the output stage of the receiver.

Remember that a transistor, unlike a vacuum tube, may be biased by a part or by all of the output current of another transistor. This is particularly true of the d-c coupled amplifier.

This method of biasing is used particularly where both PNP and NPN transistor types are contained in the same piece of equipment.

A major obstacle to the use of the d-c amplifier is that each stage controls the bias of the following stage and any change in transistor conduction caused by temperature changes or shifts in component value will also be amplified. When a number of stages are employed, compensating for bias changes becomes a definite design problem.

Many amplifiers use a combination of R-C, transformer, and d-c coupling arrangements to obtain the best features of each.

R-F AND I-F AMPLIFIERS

The r-f or i-f amplifier employs transformer coupling between stages. The impedance match from one stage to the next is of prime importance; for this reason the i-f transformers of a transistor radio are quite different from those in vacuum-tube receivers.

The i-f amplifier circuit shown in Fig. 4-10 incorporates a tapped-primary i-f transformer, single-slug tuning, low-impedance untuned secondary, and feedback to the base.

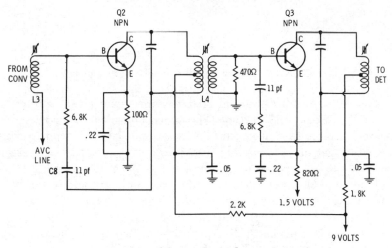

Fig. 4-10. An i-f amplifier with single-tuned transformers.

The impedances of tuned circuits are high compared to the collector and base impedances. The former are matched by using a tapped-primary i-f transformer. Only a portion of the total impedance of the tuned circuit exists from collector to ground. A secondary

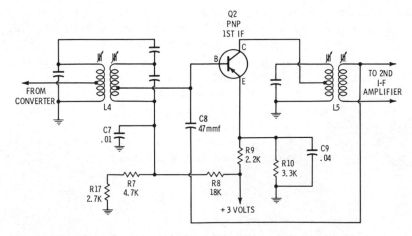

Fig. 4-11. An i-f amplifier with double-tuned transformers.

winding must have even lower impedance, since it must drive the base of a common-emitter circuit. Untuned secondary windings are normal in transistor receivers, although some double-tuned (primary and secondary) i-f transformers will be encountered.

A double-tuned i-f transformer is shown in Fig. 4-11. Both the primary and the secondary are tapped at impedance points that will match the collector of the converter to the base of the first i-f stage. Double-tuned transformers are not generally used in the personal-sized portable receivers because of the added weight and size. One double-tuned transformer may be used in a receiver, between the mixer and the first i-f amplifier, to provide a greater degree of isolation between the oscillator and the first i-f stage than a single-tuned transformer will provide.

Neutralization

In the circuits in Fig. 4-10 and Fig. 4-11, a small-value capacitor C8 is connected from the output of transistor Q2 to the input circuit of the same transistor. Capacitor C8 is a neutralizing capacitor and cancels the effect of the base-to-collector capacitance. The principle is identical to the neutralizing of a triode vacuum tube in a tuned r-f amplifier.

The transistor is also a three-element device that must be neutralized when it is used as a tuned r-f amplifier. When both the input and output of a transistor amplifier stage are tuned to the same frequency, voltages and currents are built up across the tuned circuits. The phases of these voltages and currents at resonance are such that a positive feedback occurs from the collector to the base through the base-to-collector capacitance.

Capacitor C8 (Figs. 4-10, 4-11) couples a signal, that is nearly 180 degrees out of phase with the signal on the collector, from the output circuit back to the base of the transistor. Cancellation is not complete. The feedback is only enough to keep the stage from oscillating when the input and output circuits are tuned to resonance at the intermediate frequency.

A circuit designed to operate with a neutralizing network will break into oscillation if the capacitor is open, missing, or is the wrong value. The i-f strip of such a receiver cannot be aligned until the correct neutralizing capacitor is inserted.

Automatic Volume Control (avc)

The audio output of a receiver can be controlled by affecting the gain of the i-f amplifiers. In a transistor receiver, the gain of the i-f amplifier depends upon (1) the gain of the individual transistor and

(2) the impedance match between each stage. Both can be changed by varying the voltage applied to the transistor and the current in the transistor.

When the bias current in a transistor is reduced, the gain of the transistor drops and the output and input impedances rise. The impedance rises because of the rise in collector voltage due to the reduced conduction in the transistor. (Refer to Forward and Reverse Bias in Chapter 1.) The impedance change causes a mismatch between stages and lowers the i-f amplifier gain.

The current necessary to produce this lower gain is derived from the detection of the i-f signal. The detector is generally a diode that serves as an avc diode and as an audio detector. The circuits in Fig.

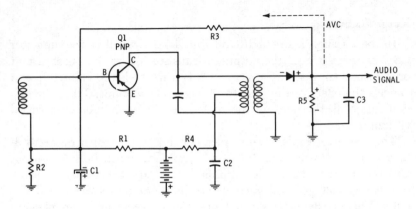

(A) System with a PNP transistor.

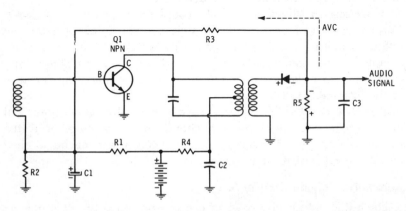

(B) System with an NPN transistor.

Fig. 4-12. Simplified versions of an avc system.

4-12 show a simplified version of an i-f stage, an avc detector, and the avc path to the transistor base. In Fig. 4-12A the rectified current through the diode changes the potential on the transistor base. The base of the PNP transistor normally is negative. A positive potential will reduce the current or will move the base potential nearer to that of the emitter.

An NPN transistor stage is shown in Fig. 4-12B. The voltage and current are the reverse of the PNP circuit. Current at the anode of the detector produces a negative voltage that moves the base in a negative direction or toward cutoff.

An increase in signal level will increase the detector output, and the increased detector potential will reduce the current in the base circuit. Two actions result: (1) the current through the transistor is reduced and (2) because the IR drop across R4 is reduced, the voltage rises at the collector terminal.

Resistor R4 and capacitor C2 in Fig. 4-12 isolate this i-f stage from the other stages and from the common supply line.

As previously stated, the change in output impedance affects the gain of the stage. The output impedance of transistor Q1 in Fig. 4-12 will be determined by the current in the transistor and by the voltage between emitter and collector.

The collector current is controlled by the avc current generated by the detector. This collector current must exist in resistor R4; as the transistor current is reduced, the collector potential rises and the output impedance of transistor Q1 therefore increases.

The range of avc action is extended by placing a diode across the primary of an i-f transformer. Fig. 4-13 is the i-f portion of a receiver that contains a 1N60 diode as part of the avc circuitry.

The cathode of the 1N60 is connected to the high side of the first i-f (converter) transformer L3. The anode terminal of the diode is connected to the tap on the second i-f transformer L4. This tap is at r-f ground potential and, therefore, the diode is, in effect, across the primary terminals of L3.

When no signal is present at the receiver input, the potential across the diode is equal to the difference between the collector voltages of Q1 (+8 volts) and Q2 (+7 volts) or 1 volt of reverse bias. When biased in reverse, a diode has an extremely high resistance, but this high resistance across the primary of the transformer does not greatly affect the Q of the tuned circuit.

The diode resistance decreases as the forward current increases. The resistance change of a 1N60 with respect to bias voltage is shown in Fig. 4-14. The resistance has been calculated from the voltage and current readings taken by using the circuit at the top of the

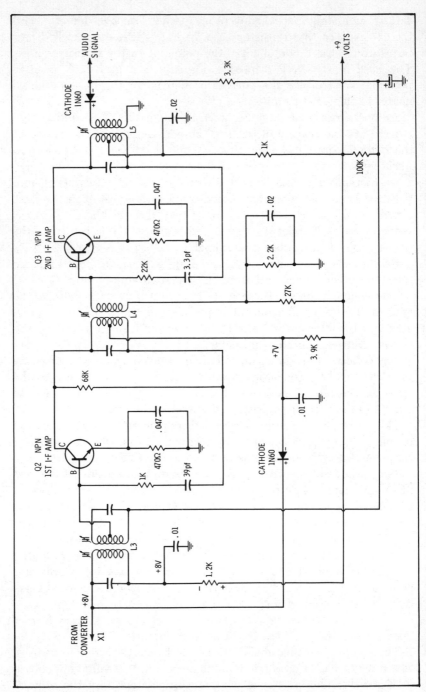

Fig. 4-13. An avc system with extended range.

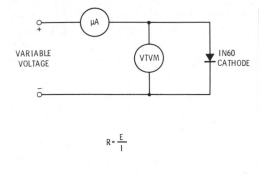

VOLTAGE	MICROAMPERES	RESISTANCE
.02	.5	40K
.04	2.5	16K
.06	5.0	12K
.08	10.0	8K
.1	20.0	5K
.12	40.0	3K
.14	70.0	2K
.16	110	1450Ω
.18	150	1200Ω
.2	200	1000Ω
.22	260	890Ω
.24	330	760Ω
.26	400	650Ω
.28	500	560Ω
.3	600	500Ω

$$R = \frac{E}{I}$$

Fig. 4-14. Resistance change of a 1N60 diode due to change of applied voltage.

chart. The characteristics listed in this chart are specific for this diode. A different type would provide different readings and for this reason a replacement diode should be the same type or a recommended substitute.

A strong signal arriving at the detector (refer to Fig. 4-13) produces a negative avc potential that is applied to the base of transistor Q2. The reduced current in the collector circuit will increase the collector voltage. When this voltage exceeds eight volts, the diode will be forward biased and will act as a low resistance.

When a resistance is placed across a tuned transformer, the transformer becomes less efficient. The diode in this circuit is a variable resistance that increases when the signal is weak and decreases when the signal is strong. The first i-f transformer efficiency is varied by the shunting effect of the 1N60 diode.

The diode reduces the gain of the receiver by lowering the gain of the i-f transformer; thus, the total range of the avc is extended beyond the range attainable if only the gain of the transistor stage were reduced.

AUDIO AMPLIFIERS

The last stage of an audio amplifier is the power output. Although this stage is an audio amplifier stage, it is different because the amplification is power gain. The output stage usually consumes more current than all the other stages. Power consumption is important, particularly to the customer, who has to purchase the batteries that supply this power.

Two output circuits serve as power stages: the single-ended (containing a single transistor) and the push-pull (containing two transistors). The single-transistor output must operate as a Class-A amplifier, whereas the push-pull arrangement can operate as Class-A, Class-B, or Class-AB (in which the operating point is somewhere between Class-A and Class-B).

Class-A operation takes place when the transistor bias sets the collector current at a point midway between design maximum and cutoff; the collector conducts current at all times. Class-B operation takes place when the collector current conducts for only half of the alternating cycle. Class-AB operation is at a point between A and B; current conduction occurs during more than half the alternating cycle, but not for the full cycle.

The class of operation is quite important for a battery operated receiver. Class-A operation requires that the full current be present in the circuit any time the receiver is on—regardless of the volume setting. Class-B operation permits a minimum of current conduction during quiescent periods and when the volume is turned down. Class-A operation consumes more battery energy but requires only one transistor. Class-B operation is more saving of battery power, but the output stage must employ two transistors.

Single-Ended Output

Fig. 4-15 shows a single transistor used as the output stage of a broadcast receiver. The transistor will be biased for Class-A operation, and current of about 8 ma will exist in the collector circuit at all times. An improper bias would distort the audio. Notice that about 80 percent of the receiver current is in the output stage.

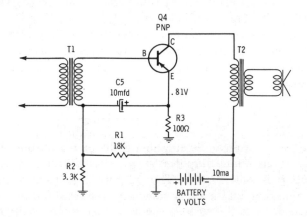

Fig. 4-15. A Class-A output stage.

It is difficult to accurately measure the bias of a transistor amplifier stage directly. However, because the collector current is greatly affected by small changes in the bias current, the collector current can be measured and will provide an indirect measure of bias. Note in Fig. 4-15 that the total current from the battery is 10 ma and (from the preceding discussion) that the output stage of the receiver consumes a large portion of this current. A change in the bias current of the output transistor will measurably affect this current reading. The transistors in the preceding stages will have little effect upon the supply current.

Voltages are the best indication of whether the current is proper or not. In Fig. 4-15, the voltage at the emitter is 0.81 volts and the emitter-resistor (R16) is 100 ohms. The current can be calculated using E/R or 8.1 ma of current in resistor R3. This is also the emitter current for the transistor.

Push-Pull Output

The push-pull circuit can be operated as Class-A, Class-B, or Class-AB. The Class-A, push-pull operation will provide only twice the power output of the single-ended, Class-A stage; and average collector current will exist at all times. The Class-B operation is very economical because almost no current exists when no signal is applied. This no-current condition is due to the transistors being biased to cutoff. However, Class-B operation causes distortion at the crossover point (the point at which one transistor ceases conduction and the other begins).

The circuits in Figs. 4-16 and 4-17 are simple forms of a push-pull circuit; current waveforms for Class-B and Class-AB operation are shown. Transformer T1 is the input and T2 is the output. The secondary of T1 and the primary of T2 are shown as separate windings for each transistor in order for the reader to maintain the thought of two separate amplifiers. Signal coupling between them is accomplished by the mutual couplings of windings A, A1, and A2 in the input circuit and windings B, B1, and B2 in the output. The battery supplies power to both sides of the push-pull arrangement. The dotted horizontal line through each of the waveforms represents the current in the circuit when no signal is applied. There will be no current in the input and output windings A and B when the signal is removed.

In the Class-B amplifier in Fig. 4-16, the transistors have zero bias. For a transistor, zero bias is equivalent to cutoff bias; and the collector current should be zero. However, because of leakage current, the collector current is not completely cut off. Current induced in

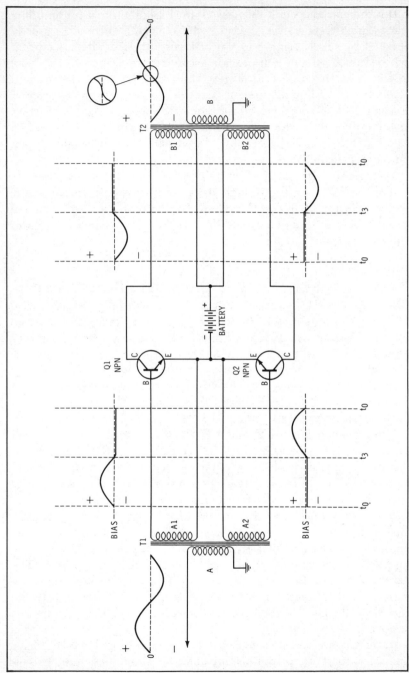

Fig. 4-16. A Class-B push-pull output stage with current waveforms. (Waveforms are not drawn to scale.)

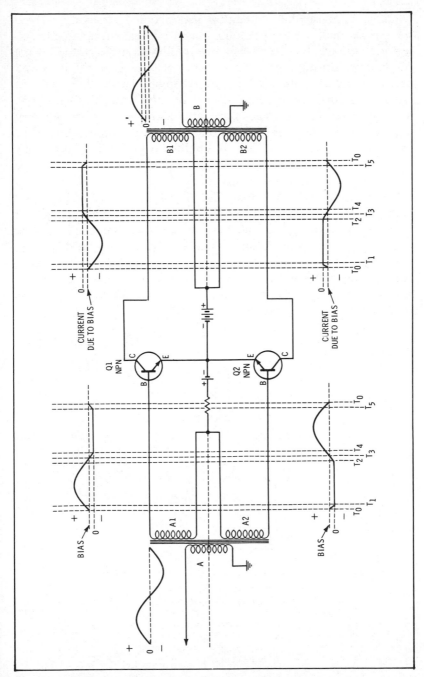

Fig. 4-17. A Class-AB push-pull output stage with current waveforms. (Waveforms are not drawn to scale.)

winding A1 causes base-to-emitter conduction in transistor Q1 on the positive half of the cycle, and this produces current in the collector and in winding B1. During this half cycle, transistor Q2 is not conducting. During the negative swing of the signal, Q1 is cut off and Q2 conducts through B2. The combined effect of currents in B1 and B2 produces the output current in winding B. One of the main disadvantages of Class-B operation is crossover distortion that is produced by the switch in conduction from one transistor to the other. For this reason, the Class-B amplifier is seldom used for audio-output stages. The abrupt change in conduction can be eliminated by using a combination of Class A and Class B features.

The arrangement shown in Fig. 4-17 is a Class-AB, push-pull amplifier that is biased to permit current in the collector circuit when no signal is applied. The positive half of the input signal drives transistor Q1 into conduction at time zero. Between t_0 and t_1, transistor Q2 is also conducting. At t_1, transistor Q2 reaches cutoff. During the time from t_1 to t_2, transistor Q1 reaches maximum conduction and then decreases. At t_2, transistor Q2 begins to conduct again. Both transistors are conducting between t_2 and t_3.

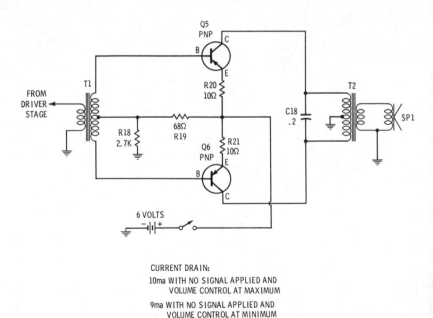

CURRENT DRAIN:

10ma WITH NO SIGNAL APPLIED AND
VOLUME CONTROL AT MAXIMUM

9ma WITH NO SIGNAL APPLIED AND
VOLUME CONTROL AT MINIMUM

18ma WITH SIGNAL APPLIED AND
NORMAL VOLUME

Fig. 4-18. A push-pull output stage, showing current drain at various volume-control settings.

The beginning of the negative half of the signal is at t_3. At this time, transistor Q1 is decreasing conduction and Q2 is increasing. At t_4, transistor Q1 reaches cutoff. During the time between t_4 and t_5, transistor Q2 reaches maximum conduction, and then decreases. At t_5, transistor Q1 begins to conduct again. Both transistors are conducting when t_6 is reached. The currents of windings B1 and B2 combine to form the output current in winding B. The dotted lines in the output waveforms show the portion of the cycle during which both transistors were conducting. The change from the positive to the negative portion of the cycle is smooth, and crossover distortion is greatly reduced. This is the push-pull arrangement most used in power-output stages. The power dissipated by the transistors is very small during a no-signal condition, but increases as the signal increases.

The output circuit of a broadcast receiver is shown in Fig. 4-18. This receiver, powered with a 6-volt battery, conducts 9 ma when the volume control is turned to minimum. At a normal volume level, the current conduction is about 18 ma. It is apparent that the volume at the speaker determines the power drain from the battery. The change in battery current will be greater for receivers that have the lowest battery voltage, and receivers with higher voltage batteries will have a smaller current change.

5

OSCILLATORS

The basic configurations for the three oscillator circuits were described and shown in Chapter 3. In this chapter we will discuss the practical circuits for each configuration and how they are used.

1. Common-emitter circuit—sometimes used in the converter stage of a superheterodyne receiver. However, this circuit is used almost exclusively in separate oscillators.
2. Common-base circuit—acts extensively as the oscillator portion of the converter in the superheterodyne receiver.
3. Common-collector circuit — seldom used as an oscillator in broadcast receivers, but is found in other equipment; for that reason the circuit will be discussed here.

Each of the three transistor-oscillator circuits is shown in its basic form in Figs. 5-1, 5-2, and 5-3. The components needed to provide bias to the transistors have been deleted, and only the most basic elements are shown. Only capacitively and inductively tuned circuits are shown because they will be encountered most often. The other frequency control systems are less often used and then are generally employed for special purposes.

FREQUENCY CONTROL

If the input, output, or feedback circuits of an oscillator are frequency selective, the circuit will tend to oscillate at one particular frequency. A number of systems that produce a controlled frequency are listed:

1. The tuned circuit—composed of a capacitor and inductor that resonate at a particular frequency.
2. The RC or RL type—frequency is controlled by the length of time a capacitor or an inductor takes to discharge through a resistance.
3. Phase-shift type—the phase relation between the input and output signal is controlled. The two signals are in phase at only one frequency. The Wien-bridge oscillator is an example of this system.
4. Crystal—frequency is controlled by the piezoelectric properties of certain crystals, such as quartz and Rochelle salt.
5. Electromechanical systems—a mechanical device such as a tuning fork is driven electrically and the mechanical vibration rate controls the frequency of the oscillator.
6. Synchronizing systems—the oscillator is adjusted close to the desired frequency, and an external signal is applied in such a manner that the oscillator synchronizes itself to the incoming frequency.

An oscillator consists of the following: (1) an amplifying device (in our case, a transistor), (2) a power source to replace I^2R losses, (3) a feedback arrangement to cause oscillation, and (4) a frequency-selective system.

COMMON-EMITTER OSCILLATOR

A common-emitter oscillator is shown in Fig. 5-1A. The transformer (coils L1 and L2) transfers energy from the output to the input. The current change in the output, or coil L1, is transferred to coil L2 and, hence, to the base of the transistor.

Coil L1 in Fig. 5-1A is tuned by capacitor C1. Coils L1 and L2 are so designed that maximum feedback occurs at the resonant frequency of the tuned circuit. The impedances of coil L2 and of the tapped portion of the tuned circuit produce a reasonably good impedance match at the oscillating frequency.

The impedance match in a transistor circuit can vary a great deal before the operation of the oscillator is upset. This fact permits wide-tolerance components to be used for design and replacement.

The circuit in Fig. 5-1B shows a method of coupling coils L1 and L2 to a separate tuned circuit. The mutual coupling between the

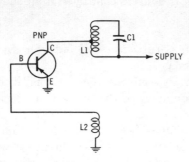 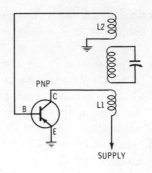

(A) *Tuned circuit in supply lead.*   (B) *Separate tuned circuit.*

Fig. 5-1. Common-emitter oscillator circuits.

three windings causes the energy transfer between L1 to L2 to be maximum at the resonant frequency of the tuned circuit. The tuned circuit need not be directly connected to the circuit to effectively control the frequency.

COMMON-BASE OSCILLATOR

Fig. 5-2 shows two methods of connecting the common-base oscillator. The tuned circuit (L1 and C1) in Fig. 5-2A is in the output, or collector circuit; and the tap point on coil L1 goes to

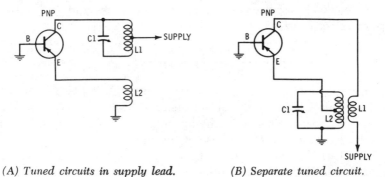

(A) *Tuned circuits in supply lead.*   (B) *Separate tuned circuit.*

Fig. 5-2. Common-base oscillator circuits.

the supply voltage. The arrangement in Fig. 5-1A was quite similar, but both the direction of current in coil L1 and the phase of the feedback signal in coil L2 were reversed. If we assume that the coils in Figs. 5-1A and 5-2A are indentical, then the phase reversal is proper, because the feedback is applied to the base in Fig. 5-1A and to the emitter in Fig. 5-2A.

Another arrangement of the common-base oscillator is shown in Fig. 5-2B. The input (emitter) is tuned and the collector is untuned. Operation of the oscillator follows the same line of reasoning as the previous ones. Circuits may differ because of design considerations such as keeping d-c voltage off the tuning capacitor; thus, the stator of the tuning capacitor can be grounded.

COMMON-COLLECTOR OSCILLATOR

The common-collector circuit is seldom employed as the oscillator in broadcast receivers. One form of this oscillator is shown in Fig. 5-3. The output signal is developed in the tuned circuit of L1 and C1. Coil L2 receives a portion of this energy and supplies it to the base. The impedance of the winding from tap to ground of coil L1 and the impedance of coil L2 produce a reasonably good impedance match between the emitter and the base circuits.

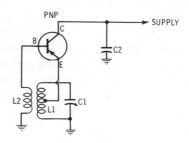

Fig. 5-3. A common-collector transistor oscillator circuit.

An important use of the common-collector oscillator is in the inverter-type power supply or in applications that require the use of power transistors. The common-collector configuration makes it possible to ground the collector or (if a push-pull oscillator) both collectors can be grounded. The transistors can be electrically and mechanically connected to the chassis, so that the chassis can act as a heat sink.

CONVERTER

The converter stage of a transistor broadcast receiver (as this book is being written) is a three-element device operating as a mixing amplifier and a local oscillator. When operating as a converter, the transistor is a nonlinear amplifier and, as such, performs a third function, that of mixing or heterodyning the received signal with the oscillator frequency. This mixing produces, among other frequencies, an intermediate frequency signal (i-f signal) that contains all the information of the original signal.

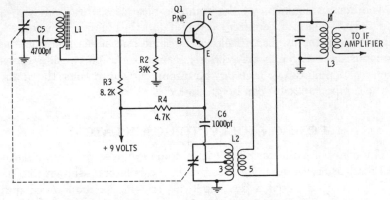

Fig. 5-4. A converter stage of a broadcast receiver.

Fig. 5-4 shows a converter stage of a broadcast receiver. Transistor Q1 is used in two circuit configurations at the same time. The collector circuit is the output circuit for both configurations. The oscillator portion operates as a common-base circuit, and mixing amplification is accomplished by a common-emitter circuit.

This dual role of the transistor is practical because a parallel-tuned circuit presents a low impedance to the passage of frequencies that are different from the resonant frequency of the LC combination. The antenna circuit is virtually a short circuit to the oscillator frequency, and the oscillator tuned circuit acts as a short circuit to the incoming r-f signal.

Oscillator

While referring to the schematic in Fig. 5-4, notice that the base of the transistor is connected to antenna coil L1. This tuned circuit has a very low impedance at the oscillator frequency; therefore, the base is grounded as far as the oscillator is concerned. Resistors R2 and R3 compose a divider to supply a d-c bias to the base of transistor Q1.

The input terminal for the oscillator is the emitter, and the output terminal is the collector. The transistor operates as a grounded-base oscillator. The feedback signal for the oscillator is obtained from the output circuit through tuned transformer L2. Tap No. 3 on the transformer is required to match the low impedance of the emitter or input circuit.

The i-f transformer L3 is in series with transformer L2, but is tuned to a much lower frequency than either the oscillator signal or the received signal. Therefore, the i-f transformer presents very little impedance to the oscillator signal. Actually, terminal No. 5 on transformer L2 is effectively grounded by transformer L3. The oscillator in Fig. 5-4 is similar to the basic oscillator in Fig. 5-2B, the difference being in the addition of components necessary to set an operating bias for transistor Q1.

Mixer Amplifier

By a line of reasoning similar to that used for the oscillator, we can consider the mixer-amplifier portion of the converter in Fig. 5-4 as being a grounded-emitter circuit. The tuned circuit of L2 in the emitter-to-ground path is tuned to the frequency of the oscillator and therefore provides a good r-f signal ground for the emitter.

Incoming signals are applied between the base and ground by antenna coil L1. Capacitor C5 acts as a d-c blocking capacitor and maintains an operating bias on the transistor. Blocking capacitor C6 places the emitter at signal ground for received signals, but blocks the direct current from ground.

Output

A great many frequencies are present in the output of the converter, but only two of them are important in the operation of the superheterodyne receiver. These are the oscillator frequency and the difference, or intermediate, frequency.

The oscillator-frequency energy is coupled back to the input by transformer L2 of Fig. 5-4. This transformer offers very little resistance to the passage of the 455-kc i-f signal. Transformer L3 is tuned to 455 kc and reacts to the i-f energy in the collector circuit.

Transformers L2 and L3 react to the oscillator frequency and the i-f signal only, and the output or collector circuit is effectively grounded to all other frequencies.

Common-Emitter Converter

The circuit in Fig. 5-5 is a converter that functions as a common emitter for both the r-f amplifier and the oscillator. In this circuit, the energy from the antenna tuned circuit L1 and from the oscillator tuned circuit L2 are picked up by separate windings. These two windings are connected in series, and the signals from both are impressed on the base of the transistor.

The output is also a series arrangement of the two tuned circuits L2 and L3. Energy at the oscillator frequency is returned to the base through transformer L2, and the i-f energy is extracted by transformer L3.

The oscillator in Fig. 5-5 operates much like the oscillator circuit in Fig. 5-1A.

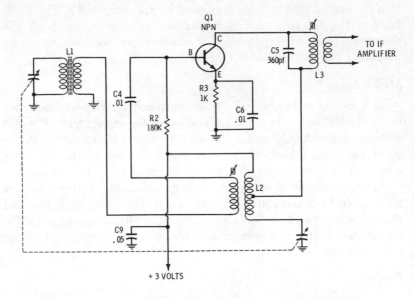

Fig. 5-5. Converter stage using the common-emitter configuration.

MIXER AND OSCILLATOR

Receivers employing a mixer and separate oscillator contain two transistors, one for the mixer and the other for the oscillator. The mixer is a nonlinear amplifier in which r-f and oscillator signals are mixed to produce the difference, or i-f, signal.

The oscillator is nearly always a grounded-emitter type. The circuits in Figs. 5-6 and 5-7 show two oscillator-circuit arrangements. The circuit in Fig. 5-6 shows a common-emitter circuit that employs an oscillator transformer with three windings. The output (collector) winding is tuned. Two other windings provide oscillator feedback and mixer injection. The winding for oscillator injection to the mixer is connected directly to the mixer input, and the agc voltage is supplied through this winding. Only one of the windings of coil L2 needs to be tuned—the mutual coupling between coils causes the resonant effect to be present in all three windings.

The oscillator in Fig. 5-7 is also a common-emitter circuit, but with a tapped coil that provides feedback and injection signals. Note that tap No. 4 is grounded for signal frequencies by bypass capacitor C9. Grounding of this point causes a signal of the correct polarity to appear at tap No. 2 supplying the base of the oscillator. Capacitor C6 couples the oscillator signal to the mixer.

68

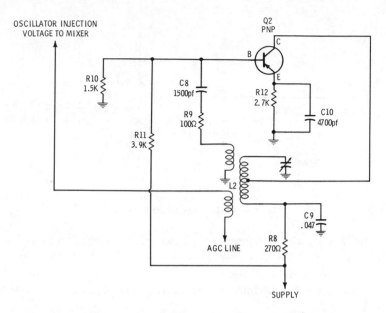

Fig. 5-6. A common-emitter oscillator circuit using a three-winding coil.

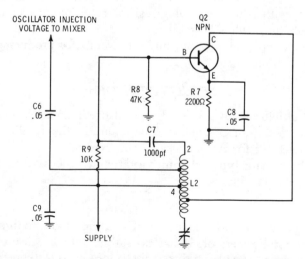

Fig. 5-7. A common-emitter oscillator circuit using a
single, tapped, coil.

PHASE-SHIFT OSCILLATORS

The phase-shift oscillator (Fig. 5-8) is simple to construct, stable
in operation, and produces a good sinewave output.

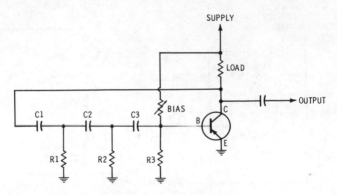

Fig. 5-8. Basic phase-shift oscillator.

The phase-shift oscillator is composed of an amplifier and a phase-shift network. The amplifier must be capable of overcoming the losses in the network. This requires that the gain of the transistor be approximately 30 times or better depending upon the network used.

The network, composed of C1, C2, C3 and R1, R2 and R3 provides a phase shift of 180° in order to produce positive feedback. In this case each of the three capacitor/resistor combinations supplies 60° phase shift for a full 180° total.

This is probably one of the simplest circuits for producing a sine-wave oscillation.

MULTIVIBRATORS

The multivibrator is a special type of oscillator used as a timing oscillator, generator of square waves, and in the familiar role of sweep generator for the television scan system.

The three main types of multivibrator are the astable, bistable, and monostable.

Astable

The astable type (Fig. 5-9) is the free running multivibrator used as a waveform generator. It has no stable state because once it is turned on, one transistor will conduct more current than the other.

Let's start with transistor Q1 in the nonconducting state—the voltage on the collector of transistor Q1 will approach the supply voltage and this minus signal will be coupled to the base of transistor Q2. The capacitor (C1) will be charged through the base-to-emitter junction of transistor Q2. This condition is shown in Fig. 5-9.

70

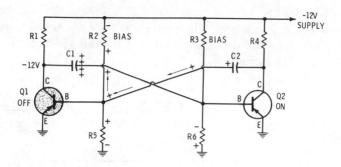

Fig. 5-9. Astable multivibrator.

Capacitor C2 is discharging through resistors R2 and R5. When the capacitor is discharged, the voltage across R5 will be controlled by the bias current in R2 and R5. Transistor Q1 will then turn on due to the negative voltage at the base, the collector voltage will drop toward zero and C1 will start to discharge through resistors R3 and R6. Transistor Q2 will be cut off and transistor Q1 will conduct.

The conducting and cutoff states will continue to switch so long as power is applied to the circuit.

Monostable

The circuit of Fig. 5-10 is a monostable multivibrator. It has one stable state in which transistor Q1 is conducting and transistor Q2 is turned off. This type multivibrator requires a trigger pulse to initiate a change in conduction state after which the circuit will return to the condition shown in Fig. 5-10.

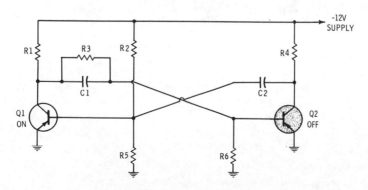

Fig. 5-10. Monostable multivibrator.

The bias for the base of transistor Q2 is obtained from the collector of the "on" transistor. The voltage at the collector of transistor Q1 is nearly zero and not enough current is available to turn Q2 on unless Q1 is first turned off.

Bistable

The circuit of Fig. 5-10 is a bistable multivibrator. The bias for the base of each transistor is derived from the collector of the

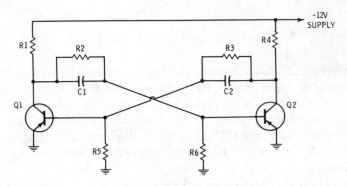

Fig. 5-11. Bistable multivibrator.

opposite transistor. This circuit has two stable states—either transistor can remain in the on condition and the other will remain off. This effect is caused by having the bias for both transistor bases supplied from the opposite transistor.

There are many variations of these three multivibrator types depending upon the purpose for which they are used. One of the main applications of the multivibrator is in computer circuits. In some of these applications it is almost impossible to recognize the multivibrator.

6

TEMPERATURE CONSIDERATIONS

The operating characteristics of a transistor depend upon the temperature at which the transistor is operating. For most transistors and other semiconductors, this temperature is the same as that of the environment in which we live and work. This will average somewhere between seventy and eighty degrees Fahrenheit (about twenty-one to twenty-seven degrees centigrade). The operating temperature for a transistor is listed in one or more of three ways—ambient, case and junction.

TEMPERATURE SPECIFICATIONS

The fact that the transistor is extremely sensitive to temperature change makes the temperature specifications important. Let's consider each of the methods of designating temperature.

Ambient Temperature

This term refers to the air or substance surrounding the transistor. For example, your transistor portable will operate at room temperature with a free flow of air. The transistors operate at an ambient temperature of about 25° centigrade (77°F). But remember that the designer probably used a figure of about 66° centigrade for the ambient temperature because the receiver may be operated on the dash of your car in summer sun and the temperature could be as high as 150° Fahrenheit.

This brings up the point of *derating factor*. This is also part of a transistor specification. For example; a transistor that will dissipate 150 mw at 25°C has a derating factor of 2 mw/°C. In the portable receiver we discussed, the increase over room temperature is 41°C (66° minus 25°) and at 2 mw per degree the transistor can only dissipate 68 mw (150 minus 82). If this is not taken into consideration, the receiver would fail at the higher temperatures.

Remember that the ambient temperature is the temperature of the surrounding air or medium, and the derating factor designates the amount by which the power must be reduced due to increased operating temperature.

Case Temperature

This term is usually applied to power transistors that are designed for mounting to a heat sink. The case temperature designated in the specifications is measured at the transistor surface that is to be in contact with the heat sink.

A power transistor must also be derated when the case temperature exceeds a given value—usually 25° centigrade. Fig. 6-1 shows

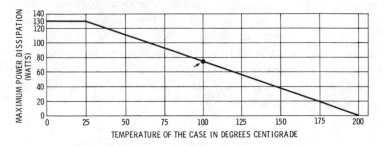

Fig. 6-1. Power versus temperature derating curve.

a derating curve for a silicon transistor with a maximum case temperature of 200° centigrade and a maximum power dissipation of 130 watts at a case temperature of 25° centigrade. For a case temperature of 100°, the power dissipation of this transistor should not exceed 74.3 watts. The derating factor for this transistor in watts per degree centigrade (W/°C) is 130/200 — 25 or .743 watts/°C.

Junction Temperature

This measurement is the maximum temperature of the semiconductor material and cannot be measured directly. For this reason the thermal resistance of the case must be used to arrive at the maximum power dissipation.

The thermal resistance of a material is defined as the temperature produced between two surfaces as a result of heat passing through the material. The thermal resistance is equal to the temperature difference divided by the wattage (°C/W).

To calculate the temperature of the junction when the thermal resistance and the power dissipation are known, let's assume that a transistor is dissipating 5 watts, the case temperature is 25°C, and the thermal resistance between the junction and the case (°C/W) is 35. Then 35 is equal to the difference in temperature between the case and the junction, divided by the 5 watts; $35 = °C/5$ or $°C = 5 \times 35$. The temperature difference between the junction and the outside of the case is 175°C.

The temperature of the case is at 25°C and this temperature plus the 175°C equals 200°C for a junction temperature. This example is for a silicon transistor that has a maximum junction temperature of 200°C. This transistor can dissipate 5 watts provided that the temperature of the case does not exceed 25°C.

It may appear that the coverage given to temperature specifications is excessive but the fact is that the operation of a transistor circuit is highly dependent on temperature.

TEMPERATURE EFFECTS

Table 6-1 lists the degrees centigrade from zero to two hundred twenty-five and the corresponding Fahrenheit temperatures. The centigrade scale is used for nearly all measurements involving transistor characteristics. The Fahrenheit temperature scale is by far the more familiar, since it is used in everyday living. Table 6-1 will be a help in correlating the two temperature scales.

Transistor characteristics are measured at a particular temperature because they change when the temperature changes. The effect of temperature on a transistor or other semiconductor junction can be shown by the following procedure.

First obtain a transistor and a fairly sensitive ohmmeter. Since the transistor can be damaged by overheating, it is best to use a low-cost unit. The voltage of the ohmmeter batteries should not exceed the maximum voltage rating of the transistor. Set the ohmmeter on one of the high scales (×10K or ×100K), and touch the ohmmeter leads to the base and collector terminals of the transistor; then reverse the leads. Attach the leads to the transistor in the position that gives the highest resistance reading, and set the multiplier

Table 6-1. Degrees of Temperature in Centigrade and
Corresponding Values in Fahrenheit.

C°	F°	C°	F°	C°	F°	C°	F°	C°	F°
0	32.0							100	212
1	33.8	26	78.8	51	123.8	76	168.8	105	221
2	35.6	27	80.6	52	125.6	77	170.6	110	230
3	37.4	28	82.4	53	127.4	78	172.4	115	239
4	39.2	29	84.2	54	129.2	79	174.2	120	248
5	41.0	30	86.0	55	131.0	80	176.0	125	257
6	42.8	31	87.8	56	132.8	81	177.8	130	266
7	44.6	32	89.6	57	134.6	82	179.6	135	275
8	46.4	33	91.4	58	136.4	83	181.4	140	284
9	48.2	34	93.2	59	138.2	84	183.2	145	293
10	50.0	35	95.0	60	140.0	85	185.0	150	302
11	51.8	36	96.8	61	141.8	86	186.8	155	311
12	53.6	37	98.6	62	143.6	87	188.6	160	320
13	55.4	38	100.4	63	145.4	88	190.4	165	329
14	57.2	39	102.2	64	147.2	89	192.2	170	338
15	59.0	40	104.0	65	149.0	90	194.0	175	347
16	60.8	41	105.8	66	150.8	91	195.8	180	356
17	62.6	42	107.6	67	152.6	92	197.6	185	365
18	64.4	43	109.4	68	154.4	93	199.4	190	374
19	66.2	44	111.2	69	156.2	94	201.2	195	383
20	68.0	45	113.0	70	158.0	95	203.0	200	392
21	69.8	46	114.8	71	159.8	96	204.8	205	401
22	71.6	47	116.6	72	161.6	97	206.6	210	410
23	73.4	48	118.4	73	163.4	98	208.4	215	419
24	75.2	49	120.2	74	165.2	99	210.2	220	428
25	77.0	50	122.0	75	167.0	100	212.0	225	437

switch of the ohmmeter to the scale that places the meter needle nearest the center.

Keep the ohmmeter leads connected to the transistor, and warm the transistor by holding it between your two fingers or by placing it near a heated soldering iron. As the transistor warms up, its resistance drops. When the temperature of the transistor changes, the electrical characteristics also change.

A similar effect can be obtained by using a junction diode. In fact, diodes are used as temperature-compensating components in certain transistor circuits. The diode junction and the transistor junction are quite similar; therefore, the resistance change of a particular diode and transistor could be similar. The junction diode is often employed as a temperature-correcting device in many of the present radio receiver circuits.

Amplifier stages such as r-f, i-f, and audio preamplifiers carry very small currents, and the usual temperature changes do not create current changes great enough to damage the transistors. The power-output stages of radios and amplifiers (particularly auto radios) control a relatively large current; and, if it were not for some form of temperature compensation, the ensuing temperature increase would cause a current increase that in turn would cause a further temperature increase. This runaway condition would almost always end in the destruction of the transistor or transistors.

TEMPERATURE COMPENSATION

The increase in current that accompanies a temperature rise can be reduced by controlling the bias to the transistor. The simplest form of this type of compensation was discussed in a previous chapter under biasing of the common-emitter configuration, in which a resistor is placed in series with the emitter to produce current feedback and to control the bias on the transistor, The method also produces some degeneration of the signal and increases the number of components in the circuit. Even so, many circuits do use this system of preventing runaway in a power-output stage.

In the circuit in Fig. 6-2, a temperature-sensitive resistor R20 is added to the biasing arrangement. This resistor, or thermistor, has a negative temperature coefficient (the resistance decreases as the

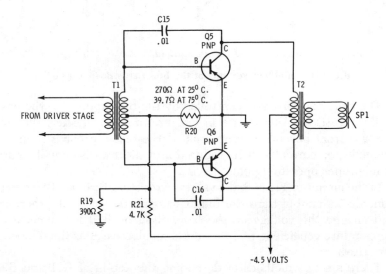

Fig. 6-2. Push-pull output stage using a temperature-sensitive resistor.

temperature rises). The cold resistance of a thermistor is supposed to be measured at 25° centigrade. The hot resistance is seldom stated, since the resistance change between cold and hot is important only to the circuit designer.

Resistor R20 in Fig. 6-2 has both its hot and cold resistances given. These are 270 ohms at 25° centigrade and 39.7 ohms at 75° centigrade. This particular thermistor has a resistance-to-temperature relation that is determined during manufacture and cannot be changed later. The effect of R20 upon the circuit can be altered by adding parallel resistances (see R19 in Fig. 6-2), series resistances, and combinations of series and parallel resistances. When the circuit is designed around different transistors and components, the thermistor that is chosen usually has entirely different characteristics.

The function of resistor R20 in Fig. 6-2 can be shown by the simplified circuit in Fig. 6-3. A single output transistor is used and the two resistors R21 and R20 make up a divider that supplies bias current to the base.

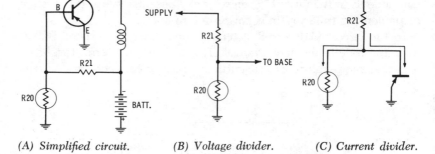

(A) Simplified circuit.   (B) Voltage divider.   (C) Current divider.

Fig. 6-3. Simplified versions of the bias network in Fig. 6-2.

The collector current is controlled by the bias applied to the base of the transistor. An increase in temperature can increase the collector current beyond the safe limit. If the bias current is reduced, the collector current will be reduced and the transistor will return to its proper operating point.

In the circuit of Fig. 6-3, the values of resistors R21 and R20 determine the amount of transistor bias. Changing the value of either one will change the voltage on the base. Resistor R20 has a negative temperature coefficient, and the resistance decreases as the temperature rises.

There are two methods of describing the action of R21 and R20 in developing transistor bias—as a voltage divider or as a current divider. This is a personal preference, and both methods are therefore given.

As a voltage divider, the two resistors can be considered a tapped bleeder with the base connected to the tap (Fig. 6-3B). Changing the value of resistor R20 will change the voltage at the tap. This voltage is applied to the base of the transistor. A rise in temperature will lower the resistance of R20, and the voltage applied to the base will decrease. The temperature rise that can cause an increase in collector current can also cause a decrease of the transistor bias, and the collector current will remain fairly constant.

As a current divider, the two resistors plus the junction are arranged as shown in Fig. 6-3C. The current in resistor R21 is divided between two paths. A rise in temperature will reduce the resistance of R20: more current will be shunted into R20, and less current will be shunted into the junction. Bias in the transistor will be reduced whenever the temperature rises.

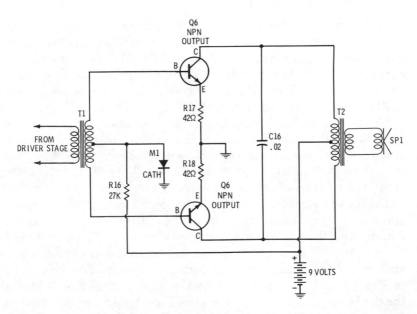

Fig. 6-4. Output circuit with diode employed for temperature compensation.

Occasionally, a diode is employed as the controlling component to prevent collector current rise. The circuit in Fig. 6-4 is an example. The characteristics of a diode and the emitter-follower action together produce temperature compensation in a circuit. A single-transistor version of this circuit is shown in Fig. 6-5.

One-tenth or two-tenths of a volt applied to a germanium diode in the forward direction will produce a relatively small current. The resistance is extremely high at very low voltages. As the voltage is further increased one-tenth of a volt, the current increases greatly. This change is nonlinear because the resistance of the diode decreases as the voltage rises. As a result, the diode can be used to obtain temperature compensation. This effect can be seen from the values given in the chart in Fig. 4-14.

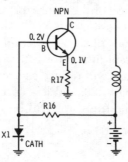

Fig. 6-5. Simplified circuit for temperature-compensating diode.

In the circuit in Fig. 6-5, the voltage impressed upon diode X1 is the same voltage impressed upon the series combination of the base-to-emitter junction and emitter resistor R17. The bias current is determined by the combination of fixed resistor R16 and the resistance of the diode. The resistance of the diode is determined by the voltage impressed across it.

The current that will exist in the base-to-emitter junction of the transistor will be determined by the voltage between base and emitter. In Fig. 6-5 the voltage is shown as 0.2 volt on the base and 0.1 volt on the emitter, or an effective bias voltage of 0.1 volt on the transistor, whereas diode X1 has a voltage of 0.2 volt across it.

The 0.1 volt across resistor R17 is developed mainly by the output current. A temperature rise will increase the collector or output current, and the voltage across R17 will increase. The potential at the emitter will rise, the difference in potential between base and emitter will be less, and the bias current will drop. For the circuits in Figs. 6-4 and 6-5, this is quite true because of the diode. Without the diode, the voltage at the base would rise because of the reduced current through R16. The current through R16 is relatively constant because the changing resistance of the diode prevents the voltage at the base from increasing too greatly. The potential on the base of the transistor rises slightly, but this rise is smaller than the increase in emitter voltage, and the bias current is reduced. The transistor bias changes as the operating temperature changes, and prevents overheating of the transistor.

HEAT DISSIPATION

The current in a transistor junction is converted into heat at a rate that can be determined by Ohm's law for power. The junction of a transistor resists the current, and the heat energy developed is determined by the quantity of this current. The heat produced at the junction must be conducted away to prevent destruction of the junction. The faster the heat is conducted away, the more efficient the transistor becomes.

Transistors used primarily for voltage amplification do not need to dissipate large quantities of heat; therefore, air is usually the only heat-conducting medium. On the other hand, the power transistor is so constructed that the metal of the junction electrically and mechanically contacts the case, and the case must be constructed of a good heat conductor, such as copper. The heat developed at the junction can be rapidly conducted away; thus, the junction can handle higher power without being damaged. The power-handling capabilities of transistors can be further improved by adding heat radiators to the transistor or by fastening the transistor to a heat sink.

RADIATOR AND HEAT SINK

The radiator and the heat sink are both descriptive of their functions. The radiator is usually a finned device, as shown in Fig. 6-6. The fins are vertical to take advantage of the fact that hot air rises.

Fig. 6-6. Finned radiator device used for heat dissipation.

As the air near the fins is warmed, it moves upward and is replaced by cooler air. This action is referred to as a "chimney" effect. Radiators of this type are shaped to provide a maximum of heat transfer with a minimum of material and space.

The heat sink is just what the name implies, a large plate or block of metal into which a large quantity of heat can sink (or be absorbed). The heat sink is usually constructed of a good heat conductor (such as aluminum) or of the metal in the equipment chassis. Two examples of heat sinks employed in automobile receivers are

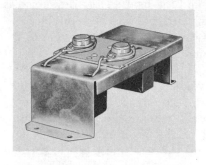 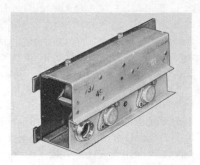

(A) *Transistors mounted on plate which is fastened to chassis.*

(B) *Chassis being used as a heat sink for the transistor.*

Fig. 6-7. Examples of heat sinks employed in automobile receivers.

shown in Fig. 6-7. The heat sinks are made of the chassis metal; but in Fig. 6-7A, the transistors are mounted on a small plate which is then fastened to the chassis. In Fig. 6-7B, the chassis is a heavy aluminum extrusion and functions as both chassis and heat sink.

Examples of the types of heat radiators used on medium power

Fig. 6-8. Clip-on heat radiators.

transistors are shown in Fig. 6-8. These types of heat radiators are used to permit a maximum of dissipation from transistors used as power output, oscillators, drivers, etc.

If a stage contains one of these radiators, DO NOT operate the equipment with the radiator removed. It is quite possible that the transistor could be damaged from overheating unless the radiator is properly replaced.

The importance of heat dissipation should not be overlooked when a transistor fails. Heat sinks and heat radiators for power transistors should be located in free air. Obstructions that stop the air circulation will cause the transistors to overheat and to be damaged.

7

MECHANICS OF
TRANSISTOR USAGE

One of the major advantages of a transistor is that it does not deteriorate and, by all rights, should last indefinitely; but this does not mean it will never fail. Transistors can fail because of excessive heat, current, voltage, and mechanical shock. Often, a transistor failure is precipitated by the failure of another component; this possibility should be investigated before a transistor is replaced. Another reason for transistor failure is improper installation of the transistor itself. This is important because another transistor has a good chance of failing if the same mistakes are repeated.

The germanium and the silicon transistor are basically the same insofar as handling and usage are concerned. The main difference is the temperature that each can withstand. The top limit for the germanium type is about 100° centigrade and the silicon type can withstand about 200° centigrade. There is less chance of causing failure of a silicon unit by overheating during a soldering operation.

TRANSISTOR REPLACEMENT
BY SOLDERING

Transistors used as low-power signal amplifiers in preamplifiers, r-f and i-f stages, etc., are connected into the circuit by inserting the leads or contacts into a socket or by directly soldering the leads into the equipment. Transistors that are plugged into the equipment (as in Fig. 7-1A) present few replacement problems, since the transistor lead arrangement and socket are usually matched. If the leads do not match the socket they can usually be bent to conform to the socket arrangement. Transistors that are soldered into the equipment (as in Fig. 7-1B) require more consideration.

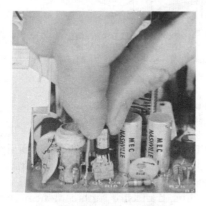

| (A) Plugged into a socket. | (B) Soldered into the circuit. |

Fig. 7-1. Two methods by which a transistor designed for low-power operation may be connected into a circuit.

The terminals or lead wires of a transistor are fastened directly to the transistor junction and are good heat conductors. When a transistor must be removed or replaced, it should be isolated from the soldering iron by a heat sink. Fig. 7-2 shows two types of heat sinks; the long-nose pliers in Fig. 7-2 are more practical, since they are usually at hand. An alligator clip is also very useful, particularly when filled with solder, as shown in the inset in Fig. 7-2. This solder increases the area in contact with the wire and adds to the volume and efficiency of the heat sink.

The quantity of solder in the connection will also determine the amount of heat required to solder or unsolder a transistor lead. A large lump of solder takes more time to melt than a smaller quantity; therefore, use as little solder as possible so that it will cool off more quickly. This leaves less chance for the transistor to heat up.

The leads of a soldered-in transistor will be flexed and bent while the transistor is being installed and removed. These leads will break, just as those on capacitors and resistors will; therefore, the transistor leads should not be moved excessively. Before removing a soldered-in transistor, make sure it actually is defective. (Suggested methods for checking the transistor are discussed in Chapter 9.) Chances are

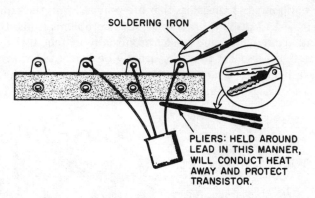

SOLDERING IRON

PLIERS: HELD AROUND
LEAD IN THIS MANNER,
WILL CONDUCT HEAT
AWAY AND PROTECT
TRANSISTOR.

Fig. 7-2. Method by which a transistor is protected from
excessive heat during installation.

that another component is bad or that a component failure ruined
the transistor. The defective component should be replaced first,
and the circuit should be rechecked. A defective part can cause a
good transistor to appear defective; thus, transistor replacement may
be unnecessary.

POWER TRANSISTORS

The power transistor is usually mounted on a heat sink or on a
radiator in order to operate more efficiently. This heat sink or radiator normally is not part of the transistor, but is added when the
transistor is mounted. Incidentally, power transistor installation is
not complete, as far as power operation is concerned, until the power
transistor is properly mounted.

The power transistor is mounted to a heat sink or radiator so that
heat is transferred away from the transistor case. One method of
mounting the transistor for maximum heat transfer is directly to the
heat sink (metal to metal); however, since the collector normally
is connected directly to the case, an unwanted potential is placed
on the heat sink. (Note: In a few circuits, the collector is grounded
so that this method of transferring heat can be used.)

In most transistor circuitry the collector must be kept above
ground. Therefore, an insulator must be placed between the transistor and the heat sink. Fig. 7-3 shows a mounting arrangement for
the TO3 power-transistor case.

In Fig. 7-3 the transistor is electrically insulated from the chassis
or heat sink by a mica, fabric, or an anodized-aluminum washer.
Mica is a very good insulator of both heat and electricity, although

heat will flow through thin sheets fairly well. When installing a mica insulator, use only one sheet, because more than one sheet will reduce the heat transferred to the heat sink and cause the transistor to overheat. Anodizing aluminum produces a thin, tough film that is a good electrical insulator, yet this film is so thin that heat is easily transmitted through it.

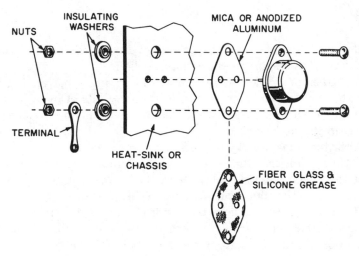

Fig. 7-3. Mounting arrangement for a power transistor.

The fabric insulator shown in Fig. 7-3 is made of glass fiber. Although it is not a good heat conductor, its heat-conducting properties can be greatly improved by filling the small openings with a silicone grease. Silicone grease, being completely inert, does not evaporate or become fluid when heated. The glass fiber pad prevents electrical contact between the heat sink and the transistor and acts as a gasket to seal in the grease. The grease provides the heat conduction necessary to cool the transistor.

Two flat surfaces placed together actually make physical contact at only a few high points. If the seemingly smooth surface were viewed under magnification, it would appear extremely rough; and two such surfaces facing each other will actually produce contact, as shown in Fig. 7-4. If the contact area can be increased, the efficiency of the heat transfer will increase. This is the purpose of the silicone grease—to fill the voids between the two surfaces.

The grease should be spread evenly over all surfaces to be contacted, in much the same way that you spread glue on surfaces to be glued together. The mica or other insulating washer should be

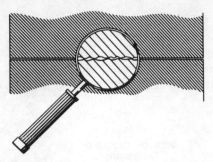

Fig. 7-4. Two apparently smooth surfaces seen under a magnifying glass.

coated on both sides, and the excess grease will be pressed out by the normal tightening of the mounting bolts.

A further precaution when you are mounting a power transistor is to be sure both surfaces are free from any bits of metal or other abrasive particles. These can damage the insulator or short the transistor to the heat sink.

After the transistor is mounted, turn on the equipment and place your fingers on the transistors. A rapid build-up of heat indicates that something is wrong. Also check the equipment at high output to make sure the transistors do not overheat.

Remember that the silicon transistor can operate normally at temperatures that will damage a germanium type. If the transistor is exceptionally hot, be sure of the type before deciding whether or not the temperature is normal.

Overheating can be caused by:

1. Incorrect transistor bias.
2. High-frequency oscillation.
3. Blocked air circulation around the radiator.
4. Improper mounting to the heat sink or radiator.
5. Defective transistor.

EXCESSIVE VOLTAGE

Voltage amplitude, voltage polarity, and voltage surges must all be considered when a transistor is placed into a circuit. When the transistor breaks down, it is very much like an electrolytic capacitor. Too much voltage can puncture a transistor, and the wrong polarity will produce excessive current and subsequent overheating. Voltage surges will produce both puncturing and overheating, the damage taking place in just an instant.

The problem of too much voltage may be encountered when an unregulated power supply is used. The battery eliminator type of power source will change the voltage as the load changes. The voltage must be reduced when the load is removed. The output of a power supply intended for transistor equipment is usually by-passed with at least a 1000-mfd capacitor. When the load is removed, the voltage increases; when the load is then replaced, it will be connected to a higher-than-normal voltage. The voltage does not drop instantly because of the high-value capacitor, which must discharge first.

When a power supply is employed with transistor equipment, turn down or turn off the supply voltage, rather than disconnect or switch off the receiver.

POLARITY

One of the interesting aspects of transistors is that we must concern ourselves with both types of units, NPN and PNP; and both have similar envelopes, with only a number to point out the difference. If we guess at the type and guess wrong, we may well have a ruined unit. Therefore, give the same consideration to a transistor that you would give to an electrolytic capacitor. Observe the polarity, NPN or PNP. Remember this important fact—the *collector* of an NPN is Positive and the *collector* of a PNP is Negative.

High voltage or a voltage with potential great enough to break down a transistor junction seldom will be found in a transistor receiver powered by the correct batteries. If the wrong batteries have been placed in the receiver, high voltage may destroy a number of transistors, although chances are the filter capacitors will short first. One of the first checks to be made on a defective radio receiver is to be sure that it contains the correct type battery. If a substitute battery is installed, be sure that the voltage of the replacement is the same as the original.

Another source of high voltage may be encountered in hybrid equipment containing both transistors and high-voltage vacuum tubes. The transistors are often powered by B+ from a voltage divider. The voltages should be checked to reveal whether any excessive voltages are present.

Voltage surges are a common source of transistor failures. The surges are generally caused by making and breaking a current-carrying circuit. Resistive circuits can be broken and replaced with little trouble; but if the circuit contains high-value capacitors or inductors, the making or breaking of circuits can cause voltage transients that will damage a transistor. The power source should be turned off before any circuit breaks or connections are made.

MECHANICAL SHOCK HAZARD

A great deal has been said about the shock resistance of the transistor. Transistors are highly shock resistant, but they can be damaged by a sharp blow or by being dropped. The statement "shock resistant" does not mean destruction-proof.

SUMMARY

When a transistor is to be removed or installed, the following considerations should be kept in mind.

Low-Power Transistors

Turn off the power source.

Observe the pin arrangement when a transistor is removed, and replace the new unit in the same manner.

When soldering transistor leads, use pliers or clips to clamp the leads and conduct the heat away from the transistor.

Make reasonably sure a transistor is defective before unsoldering it.

Power Transistors

Turn off the power source.

Use the recommended method for mounting, or mount the replacement the same way as the one removed.

Addition of silicone grease to any mounting system will improve the performance of any unit, and is required on many.

Check the operating temperature with the volume at a high setting. The heat rise should not be excessive.

8

RELATED
SEMICONDUCTOR
DEVICES

The transistor is only one item in a family of semiconductor devices. It is by far the most popular of the semiconductor devices and as such the term transistor tends to be interpreted as meaning any semiconductor device.

Many persons tend to think of all semiconductor devices as transistors, whereas many of the devices have individual identities. Among these types are the silicon controlled rectifier (scr), the tunnel diode (td), and the Zener diode (also referred to as a breakdown diode, avalanche diode, and voltage regulator diode).

The term transistor should be reserved for those devices that perform transistor (transfer + resistor) functions. Among these are the junction transistor, field effect transistor (fet) and the unijunction transistor (ujt).

ZENER DIODES

If you were to subject a Zener diode to a series of tests for a diode the results would be rather disappointing because you would find you have a normal silicon rectifier. The Zener diode has a normal forward-conduction characteristic, a high-resistance blocking state and a peak inverse voltage rating (piv). Normally you would not exceed the piv rating because the diode would break down and probably be damaged, but, this is the area in which the Zener diode is designed to operate.

A characteristic curve for a Zener diode is shown in Fig. 8-1. The curve to the right of the center line is the same as that for a silicon rectifier or diode. The curves to the left are the same as regular silicon diodes except that the Zener diode is designed to operate in this region. The standard silicon diode can also operate in the Zener mode (beyond the piv rating) but it may be damaged.

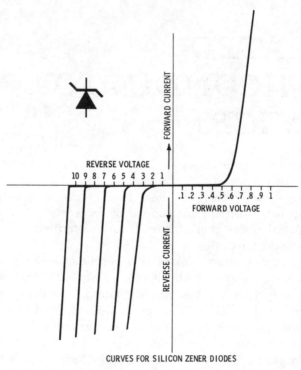

CURVES FOR SILICON ZENER DIODES

Fig. 8-1. Curves for silicon Zener diodes.

The operation of the Zener diode is nearly the same as the gas type of voltage-regulator tube. When a voltage is applied to a Zener diode in the reverse direction it develops a high resistance. When the voltage is increased to the Zener or break-down point, the current suddenly increases. The current increase is usually limited by an external resistance that prevents the current from increasing beyond a predetermined point. The basic applications of the Zener diode, in most instances, will be nearly identical to those for the gaseous-regulator tube.

A shunt regulator circuit is shown in Fig. 8-2. Resistor R1 is used to produce a voltage drop between the d-c source and the diode regulator. R1 should be chosen to limit the current through the diode

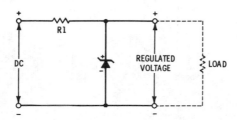

Fig. 8-2. Shunt regulator circuit.

to the rated maximum when the load is removed. When the load is connected across the diode, the current will be divided between the diode and the load. The voltage across the diode and load will remain relatively constant over a given range of changing load conditions.

The applications for the Zener diode exceed those for the gas type voltage regulator because of the reduced size and the almost limitless range of Zener voltages that are available.

SILICON CONTROLLED RECTIFIER

The controlled rectifier (scr), also called a thyristor, is a four layer structure designated as PNPN and is best described as two complementary transistors connected as shown in Fig. 8-3C. The controlled rectifier is shown in Fig. 8-3A as a four-layer structure. This can be broken into the equivalent of two complementary transistors as shown in Fig. 8-3B. The polarities shown are for the conducting state. A reverse polarity is always blocked.

The transistors in Fig. 8-3C are connected so that the collector of Q1 drives the base of Q2 and the collector of Q2 drives the base of Q1. As long as the base-to-emitter junction of Q2 remains cutoff, the two transistors will remain in the blocking state.

If a small forward current is produced in the base-to-emitter junction of Q2, the transistor will conduct and the collector conduction of Q2 will produce a current in the base-to-emitter junction of Q1, turning on transistor Q1. Conduction in the collector of Q1 will drive the base of Q2 and the conduction of Q2 will increase. This positive

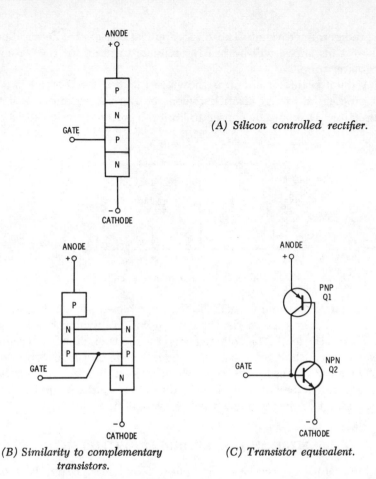

(A) Silicon controlled rectifier.

(B) Similarity to complementary transistors.

(C) Transistor equivalent.

Fig. 8-3. Silicon controlled rectifier and transistor analogy.

feedback loop will cause a rapid rise in the conduction between anode and cathode. As long as voltage is applied between the anode and cathode, the pair will continue to conduct. Turn off requires that the power be removed (or reduced below the level needed to sustain conduction) at which time the device will revert to a blocking state.

The action of the silicon controlled rectifier can also be considered as similar to the action of the thyratron. The grid can initiate the conduction through the tube but the power must be removed before it can regain a blocking state. A major advantage that the silicon controlled rectifier has over the thyratron is that the voltage drop across the unit is very small during conduction whereas there is a considerable voltage drop across the thyratron.

A schematic showing the way that an scr is connected for proper operation is shown in Fig. 8-4. The symbol for a silicon controlled rectifier (scr) is the standard diode symbol with a gate lead extending from the bar. In Fig. 8-4, the scr is shown in the off position with the gate connected to the cathode. This corresponds to transistor cutoff when the base is connected to the emitter. In some circuits a negative voltage is applied to the gate as a reverse bias to ensure complete cutoff.

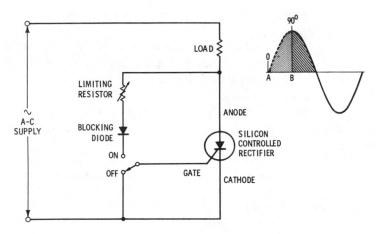

Fig. 8-4. Bias for silicon controlled rectifier.

In the on position of the switch, the gate is indirectly connected to the anode. The gate must not be connected directly to the anode because excessive current will damage the gate-to-cathode junction. A series limiting resistor is used to keep the current below the rated maximum value.

Because an alternating current is used to supply power, a blocking diode is installed to prevent the application of a high negative voltage to the gate. Typical maximums for the reverse voltage at the gate range from 5 to 15 volts.

Another method used to protect an scr from a negative overvoltage in a test circuit is to connect a silicon diode between the gate and cathode as shown in Fig. 8-5. The gate voltage cannot exceed approximately 0.6 volts under these conditions.

The silicon controlled rectifier is designed to be triggered into conduction by an applied gate signal. This signal must reach a given voltage (about 0.15 to 3.0 volts) and supply a given gate current. The current necessary to trigger the scr may be as low as a few milliamperes or range to a few hundred milliamperes depending upon the

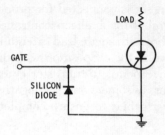

Fig. 8-5. Diode used to prevent excessive negative voltage at the scr gate.

device and the particular circuit. Typical trigger currents range from about 10 to 50 milliamperes.

Most applications for the scr are in a-c control circuits and the gate triggering is usually a phase-control arrangement. The simplest arrangement is the one shown in Fig. 8-4 with the switch in the on position. The amount of gate current is related to the amplitude of the sine wave and since maximum current will be reached at the peak of the wave it is only possible to trigger the scr on the rise of the positive swing.

If the limiting resistor is made variable, the scr can be triggered at any point between A and B on the sine wave or between 0° to 90°. This is only half of the phase control that can be achieved by a circuit such as the one in Fig. 8-6.

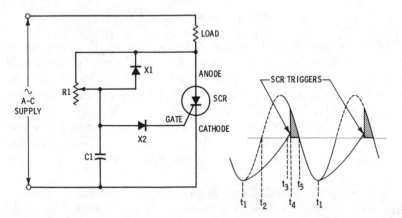

Fig. 8-6. Simplified circuit for a half-wave scr control.

In the circuit of Fig. 8-6, capacitor C1 charges through diode X1, to the full line voltage on the negative swing of the sine wave. This is indicated as point t_1. As the line voltage swings toward the zero line, capacitor C1 begins to discharge. The a-c line reaches zero volts at point t_2 but, due to the RC time constant of R1 and C1, the capaci-

96

tor discharges completely at time t_3 and begins to acquire a positive charge. The charge on C1 reaches the trigger voltage of the scr at time t_4 and discharges through diode X2 and gate-to-cathode junction of the scr. Between times t_4 and t_5 the scr is conducting. At time t_6 the line-voltage polarity reverses, the scr blocks, and capacitor C1 begins to charge through diode X1. At time t_1 another cycle is initiated.

The choice of resistor R1 and capacitor C1 is determined by one-half cycle at the line frequency. For a 60-cycle line frequency, the RC time should be approximately .01 second (1/120 second).

Diode X2, used in this circuit, is to prevent the negative charge on C1 from being applied across the gate-to-cathode junction. In a practical version of this control circuit, a current limiting resistor is usually installed between the anode of the scr and resistor R1. If this is not done, the anode will be connected to the gate when control R1 is reduced to zero. The excess current can damage the scr.

SILICON UNIJUNCTION TRANSISTOR

The unijunction transistor has a principle of operation that is considerably different from that of the junction transistor. The physical construction of the unijunction transistor is shown in Fig. 8-7A. It is composed of a single bar of high-resistivity silicon, contacted at the ends by base 2 and base 1 and containing a single PN junction located off center and closest to base 2.

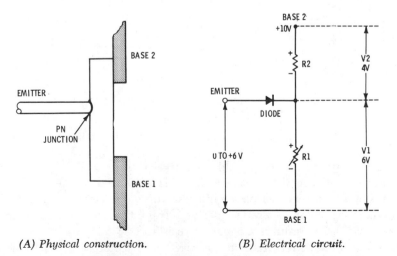

(A) Physical construction.   (B) Electrical circuit.

Fig. 8-7. Unijunction transistor.

The electrical circuit that represents this transistor is shown in Fig. 8-7B. The unijunction operates by causing the conductivity of the bar to be changed. The silicon bar is doped to be N type and a forward bias (positive applied to the emitter) applied across the emitter junction will cause positive charges (holes or minority carriers) to be injected into the bar of silicon. This lowers the resistance of the bar between the PN junction and base 1.

In Fig. 8-7B, the voltage between base 2 and base 1 is indicated as 10 volts and the division of voltage across the bar is such that 6 volts exists from base 1 to the cathode of the junction (diode). If the emitter is connected through an input circuit to Base 1, the diode will be reverse biased. In order to inject positive charges into the silicon bar, the voltage at the emitter (anode of the diode) must exceed the 6-volts existing on the cathode side of the junction. When the voltage on the emitter causes the diode to conduct, the injection of positive charges into the silicon bar causes the resistance of R1 to decrease. The 6 volts across R1 also decreases and this causes the number of carriers injected into the bar to increase. The voltage (V1) across resistor R1 decreases faster than the emitter voltage and this gives rise to a negative-resistance effect.

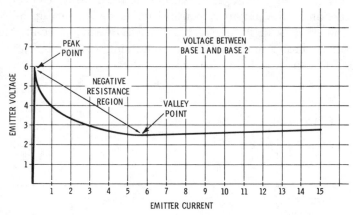

Fig. 8-8. Plot of the emitter voltage and current for a unijunction transistor.

The curve representing this negative-resistance effect is shown in Fig. 8-8. When the emitter voltage is increased to the peak-point value the current increases while the voltage decreases. Since resistance is a computed value derived from the current and voltage ($-E/I$), the result is a negative resistance.

The unijunction transistor is used as oscillator, switch, voltage sensor, phase detector, pulse generator, and a variety of other uses that are too numerous to list here. One of the simple but extremely practical circuits is shown in Fig. 8-9. This circuit is a relaxation

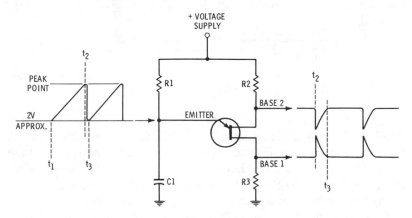

Fig. 8-9. Relaxation oscillator.

oscillator in which the frequency is determined by the RC time constant of R1 and C1. The charge and discharge curve for capacitor C1 is shown at the junction of R1 and C1. Capacitor C1 charges from the supply to the peak point as shown on the curve from t_1 to t_2. During this time the emitter junction is reverse biased and this voltage change is not present at base 1 or base 2 terminals.

When the voltage across the capacitor reaches the peak point it discharges through the emitter junction to base 1 and ground. This discharge takes place between points t_2 and t_3 and gives rise to the pulses at base 2 and base 1.

One of the interesting aspects of this device is that any one of the three terminals, emitter, base 1, or base 2 can be used as the output terminal.

FIELD EFFECT TRANSISTOR

The field effect transistor (fet) contains a current path that is modulated by an electric field. The current path is a channel of N or P type material that contains one or more PN junctions. An electric field is generated in the channel by reverse biasing the junction. The reverse bias produces a region that is depleted of all free charge carriers.

A cross section of the silicon bar and the channel between the PN junctions is shown in Fig. 8-10. The silicon bar is doped either N or P and a junction is formed at the center of the bar by using a material

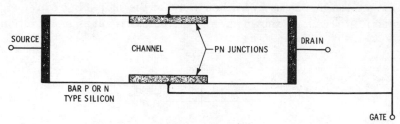

Fig. 8-10. Construction of field effect transistor.

of opposite conduction type. The area inside the junction or junctions is called a "channel." The resistance of the material in this channel is determined by the number of free charge carriers. With no voltage applied to the junction, the bar of silicon acts as a resistive element. In normal operation of the fet the junction is reverse biased.

The effect of a reverse bias on the carriers at a junction are shown in Fig. 1-5B in the first chapter. The area near the junction is depleted of current carriers and for all practical purposes this area becomes a nonconductor or insulator.

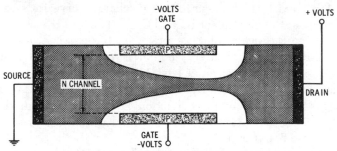

Fig. 8-11. The field effect.

In Fig. 8-11 the effect of placing a reverse bias on the PN junction causes a narrowing of the channel. The reduction of the conductive area causes an increase in the resistance between the source and the drain. In this respect the effect is somewhat similar to the effect produced in a vacuum tube when the charge around the grid prevents the charge carriers (electrons) from reaching the plate. If the reverse bias applied to the gate is increased, a point is reached where the drain current is practically cut off—actually a small current always exists.

The drain voltage, drain current, and the gate voltage are all interdependent. Observe that the nonconducting area in Fig. 8-11 extends farthest into the channel at the drain end of the bar. This is caused by the fact that the bias is greatest at the drain end. The source is ground and the drain is positive on the N-channel field effect transistor (fet). The bias is greatest between points of greatest potential; this is between the gate and drain terminals.

The characteristic curve for an fet closely represents one for a pentode tube in which the terminals of the fet are likened to those in the tube; the source is the cathode, the drain is the plate, and the gate is the grid. A curve that shows the relation between the drain volts, drain milliamperes, and the gate volts is shown in Fig. 8-12.

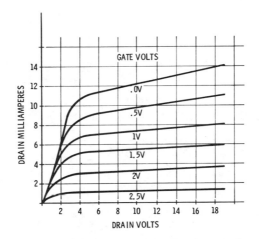

Fig. 8-12. Characteristics curve relating the drain voltage, drain current and gate volts.

The characteristics of the fet are quite similar to the low voltage vacuum tube used in automobile receivers. The fet has a high input impedance due to the fact that the gate is a reverse biased diode. The output impedance is relatively high when compared with that of a junction transistor.

Unlike the junction transistor whose basic construction requires two junctions, the fet can be fabricated with a number of gates. This permits the fet to be constructed to operate like multigrid vacuum tubes.

The fet has many of the characteristics of the vacuum tube and can be used in circuits that would normally require the use of a vacuum tube. A very practical application of the fet is to make the transformation from a high input impedance to a low output impedance. One such use is for the first stage of a solid state amplifier in which a high input impedance can be fed to the gate of the fet and the output of the fet can be used to match the input of a following transistor stage.

9

TESTING
TRANSISTORS

The transistor is the principal component in a transistor receiver; on this basis alone, one would be inclined to suspect it when a failure occurs. The transistor is, however, a very dependable component and generally fails no more, and probably less, than any other component. It is not practical to remove and test each transistor in the receiver, particularly when the transistors are probably good. Before making a wholesale attempt at testing transistors, you should check the normal operation of the transistors in the various circuits.

The servicing of transistor equipment should begin with an attempt to localize the general area of the trouble. This can be done in many ways, and each technician can apply his own particular methods. A general voltage check at various points in the equipment can sometimes locate discrepancies that may lead to the trouble. (An important point to remember is to check the battery voltage with the equipment turned on.) A signal-tracing check will also help determine the location of the trouble.

When you are checking measured voltages against those on a schematic be sure the battery or the power supply is the same voltage as that indicated on the schematic. If it is different, you will not be able to depend on the other values being correct.

Be sure that the power supply is connected in the correct polarity. If it is reversed, it is possible to damage components in the receiver. ALWAYS turn the power supply down before you connect it to the circuit to be checked. After it is connected, slowly turn up the voltage and observe the current meter. If the current is normal, turn the voltage up to the value indicated on the schematic. If the current is excessive, reduce the voltage until less than half of the normal current is indicated and then proceed to check for the trouble.

CHECKING THE TRANSISTOR AMPLIFIER

The common-emitter configuration is used for nearly all transistor circuits. The voltage at the base will be just slightly different from the voltage at the emitter, but may be plus or minus in relation to the emitter. Fig. 9-1 shows two i-f stages from a receiver, one PNP and one NPN. The collector of Q2 measures zero volts, and the collector of Q3 measures 5.1 volts. Without a schematic of this receiver, the technician might be misled by this condition, since transistors used as i-f amplifiers are usually of similar conduction types.

A check of the base and emitter voltages in this receiver will reveal that the potential is less at the base of Q2 than at the emitter, and the potential is higher at the base of Q3 than at the emitter. Both biases are correct.

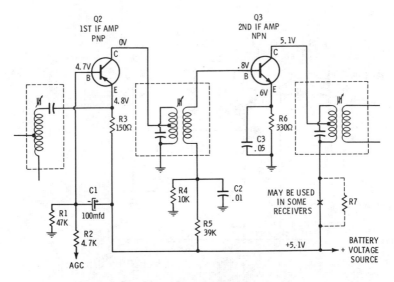

Fig. 9-1. An r-f amplifier using both PNP and NPN transistors.

Collector current can be measured by checking the voltage drop across a known resistance in the emitter or collector circuit. For example, resistor R3 in the emitter of Q2 in Fig. 9-1 is 150 ohms, and the voltage drop across R3 is 5.1 minus 4.8 or 0.3 volt. The current equals E/R, or .3/150, or 2 milliamperes. The current for transistor Q3 can be calculated by using resistor R6 in the emitter lead or a resistor such as R7 in the collector if the circuit contains one.

If the calculations place the current too high or too low, don't assume this is a true current until the resistor value has been checked and determined to be correct.

Improper transistor bias will produce an improper current in the emitter or collector circuit. The bias for transistor Q3 in Fig. 9-1 is detemined by R4 and R5. These resistors will seldom be off value because they carry very small currents; but when the bias is wrong, they should be checked.

An example of a circuit that will add confusion to the service problem is shown in Fig. 9-2. This audio driver and output circuit contains both conduction types, PNP and NPN, and both germanium and silicon types of transistor.

The bias at the base-to-emitter junction is indicated for both types. The driver (Q4) is a germanium transistor that is biased at approximately 0.2 volt. The output stage (Q5) is a silicon transistor that

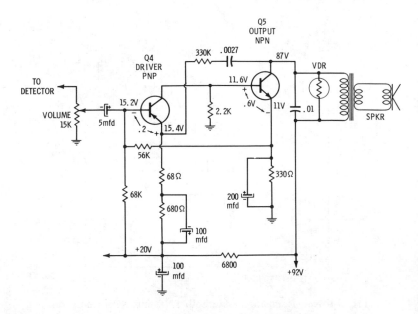

Fig. 9-2. Audio amplifier that contains both silicon and germanium transistors.

104

is biased at approximately 0.6 volt. The polarity of the bias is marked at the arrows on Fig. 9-2. The bias on a normally-operating Class-A stage will indicate the conduction (PNP or NPN) type by the voltage polarity and the transistor material (silicon or germanium) is indicated by the value of the voltage.

Notice in this amplifier that the output transistor is biased from the collector of the driver and the bias for the driver is controlled by the voltage existing at the emitter of the output stage. This is a negative-feedback arrangement in which the bias and transistor conduction tend to stabilize each other.

TESTING TRANSISTOR CURRENT GAIN

The transistor must be able to control the current in the emitter and collector circuits. Current control can be checked without removing the transistor from the circuit. Before any suspected component is removed from the circuit, the current-gain tests should be performed. These tests are applicable to any transistor amplifier, whether in the oscillator, converter, i-f, or audio circuits. The collector current should cut off when the base and emitter are shorted and a transistor should exhibit either increased or decreased conduction depending on the bias change.

Test I

Locate a resistor in the emitter or collector circuit. In Fig. 9-1, resistor R6 can be used. The reading of 0.6 volt is due to the current in transistor Q3. Short the base to the emitter. This will cut off the transistor and reduce the voltage across R6 to practically zero. A transistor that cannot be cut off is defective and should be replaced. A small voltage across the emitter resistor will be produced by the bias current. In the event a collector resistor such as R7 in Fig. 9-1 is used, the small voltage will usually be due to leakage currents. If the leakage current is excessive, the transistor should be removed and checked outside the circuit.

Test II

An additional test is to parallel one of the bias resistors with one of equal or nearly equal value. An example would be placing a 39K resistor in parallel with resistor R5 in Fig. 9-1. This would about double the emitter current, and the voltage across R6 should increase to approximately 1 volt.

Test II is not as important as Test I, but does add useful information about the operation of the transistor.

CHECKING OSCILLATORS

The oscillator section of a receiver is shown in Fig. 9-3. The collector current in transistor Q1 is approximately 0.3 ma. This is calculated by dividing the 0.45-volt drop across resistor R4 by 1,500.

When an oscillator is not operating, collector current will increase to about twice the operating value. In the circuit in Fig. 9-3, the collector current will rise to nearly 0.8 ma, and this will cause the voltage at the emitter to rise to about 1 volt.

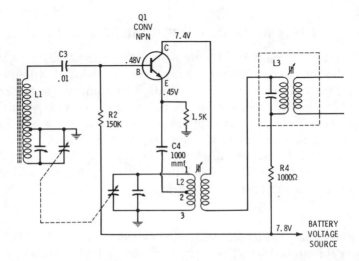

Fig. 9-3. A typical oscillator circuit in a broadcast receiver.

The oscillator can be checked by shorting the tuned section of L2 or by shorting any two of the terminals 1, 2, or 3. This will stop the oscillator and increase the collector and emitter current. If the oscillator is already inoperative, the current will be high and shorting the coil terminals will not change the current.

When an oscillator coil fails, it is either open or shorted. The open coil can be checked with an ohmmeter, but a short circuit may take place between two adjacent turns; therefore, no appreciable change in the resistance reading will be noted. Shorting two terminals of a good oscillator coil produces the same effect as a shorted coil and can be used to check oscillator operation.

Remember that lack of transistor current gain will also prevent oscillation; therefore, check the current gain of the oscillator transistor or of the converter transistor before changing other components in the circuit.

CHECKING CLASS-A AUDIO AMPLIFIERS

A single-ended audio amplifier is operated Class-A. This means the transistor is biased close to the center of the operating curve, or about halfway between design maximum and cutoff. Since most audio amplifiers have output or coupling transformers for collector loads, it is difficult to determine whether the transistor is actually biased for Class-A operation.

An audio amplifier that is improperly biased will cause the signal to be distorted at high volume levels, but at low output levels it will sound normal. The circuit should be checked for correct voltages, and the transistor should be checked for current control.

The most accurate test for Class-A operation is made with use of an oscilloscope and an audio-signal generator. The scope will show clipping of the positive or negative swings before the normal output is reached. Knowing the polarity that is clipped also indicates whether the bias is too high or too low.

CHECKING PUSH-PULL OUTPUT

The push-pull output stage usually is biased near cutoff, and current drain increases when a signal is applied. A milliammeter in series with the supply will indicate how the stage is operating. Excessive current in either or both transistors will be indicated by a high meter reading.

The individual currents can be checked by measuring the voltage across each emitter resistor. When the emitter resistor is common to both units and one transistor is suspected of being defective, one

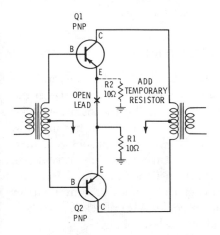

Fig. 9-4. An arrangement for checking the current balance in a push-pull output circuit.

emitter lead can be opened and another resistor of the same value placed in that lead (Fig. 9-4). The original emitter resistor R1 is not touched. The emitter lead of transistor Q1 is opened, and resistor R2 is temporarily clipped or tack soldered between the emitter terminal and ground. The current balance between the two transistors can now be checked both with and without a signal being applied to the arrangement.

A transformerless output circuit (Fig. 9-5) can be checked by using a voltmeter. As a general rule, this type of circuit is quite stable due to the feedback through R1 to the base of transistor Q1. The conduction of transistor Q1 determines the bias of the output transistors.

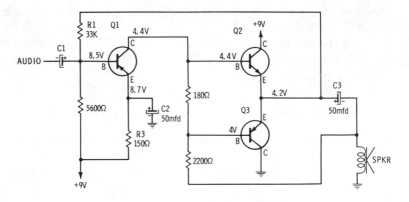

Fig. 9-5. A complementary push-pull amplifier.

The voltage at the emitters of Q1 and Q2 should be approximately one-half of the nine volt supply. A defective component will cause this voltage to change and result in distortion at increased volume levels.

OUT-OF-CIRCUIT TESTS

A rapid check of a transistor can be made with an ohmmeter. Such a procedure is shown in Fig. 9-6. Be sure the battery voltage in the meter does not exceed the voltage rating of the transistor. Also be sure not to use the low meter scales for the low-power transistor. On the high meter scales, the current between the probes is limited by high internal resistances; but on the low scales, the current can become quite high and overheat the transistor junction. If you are unsure about your ohmmeter, connect the probes to a milliameter and check the current on each ohms scale. Also check the voltage at the probe tips for each of the ohms scales.

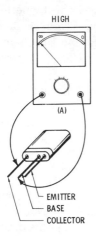

HIGH

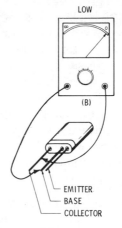

LOW

(A)

EMITTER
BASE
COLLECTOR

(B)

EMITTER
BASE
COLLECTOR

(A) Resistance measured between collector and base.

(B) Same resistance measurement as in (A), but with ohmmeter leads reversed.

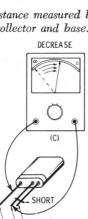

DECREASE

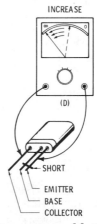

INCREASE

(C)

SHORT

EMITTER
BASE
COLLECTOR

(D)

SHORT

EMITTER
BASE
COLLECTOR

(C) Resistance measured between collector and base, with a short placed between base and emitter.

(D) Resistance measured between collector and emitter, with a short placed between base and emitter.

Fig. 9-6. Procedure for checking a transistor with an ohmmeter.

Start each test by setting the ohmmeter on the highest scale, then reduce it to the scale that produces an appropriate reading. The ×10,000 and ×100,000 scales on most meters are usually safe for checking low-power transistors. The ×1 and ×100 scales are usually correct for the high-power transistors.

Set the ohmmeter to the highest range, and connect the leads to the base and the collector terminals (Fig. 9-6A). Reverse the connections and note the direction that provides the highest reading (Fig. 9-6B). This is the reverse-bias direction. Connect the leads in this direction, observe the meter reading, and short the emitter and base terminals together as shown in Fig. 9-6C. The resistance reading should decrease.

Remove the ohmmeter lead from the base terminal and connect it to the emitter terminal. Observe the resistance reading, then short the base to the emitter (Fig. 9-6). The resistance should increase.

A defective transistor will not perform in this way. A transistor that is weak or that has high leakage will not be detected by this test. This is strictly a good-bad test.

Caution—There are a number of transistors that have emitter-to-base breakdown voltages (V_{EB}) that range as low as 0.5 volts. These are usually high frequency units used in applications such as television tuners and r-f stages in f-m and communications equipment. These types can be easily damaged by the voltage from an ohmmeter.

A number of transistor testers are available on the market. Some of these give a value reading; others give only a good-bad indication. Transistor testers are available either as separate units or combined with other test instruments, such as tube testers. For most receiver repairs, a good-bad indication is all that is required. The most positive test, however, is direct substitution of the questionable transistor.

SUBSTITUTION

A transistor can be temporarily substituted for checking circuit operation or for detecting a defective transistor. In such instances, any transistor with a similar rating can be used. Although this substitute may not work as well as the correct transistor, the fact that it does work indicates that the original transistor is defective. The defective transistor should then be replaced with one having the same type designation or a type recommended by the receiver or transistor manufacturer.

INDEX

365

11 1 321 G P 70 1

ABC's OF TRANSISTORS

by George B. Mann

To most people, the transistor is a mysterious device; this is probably because the working part of the transistor cannot be taken apart and observed. It is a solid crystal with leads—it cannot be disassembled, and nothing in it can be observed to move.

This book describes the structure of the semiconductor material and the action that takes place inside the completed crystal. The basic physical and electronic features are discussed in easy-to-understand terms.

The operating principles of many transistor circuits, such as oscillators, multivibrators, and push-pull amplifiers are discussed in detail along with practical servicing and testing procedures. One chapter introduces you to other semiconductor devices such as Zener diodes, silicon controlled rectifiers, and the unijunction and field-effect transistors.

abc's of Transistors, is written so that anyone interested in the subject can obtain a basic understanding of the principles behind these amazing devices. Therefore, this book is recommended as a beginning text for students, technicians, amateurs, and hobbyists.

HOWARD W. SAMS & CO., INC.
THE BOBBS-MERRILL CO., INC.

20440
$2.75 (In Canada $3.50)